Letters from Fred

A Novel

Books by Thomas Hanna

The Lyrical Existentialists
Bodies of Revolt
The Body of Life
Somatics

Letters from Fred

A Novel

Thomas Hanna

Freeperson Press
Novato, California

Editor: Eleanor Criswell Hanna
Copy Editor: Virginia Schmidt
Editorial Assistant: Marsha Calhoun
Cover Design: Dunham Bergquist + Associates
Cover Photo: John O'Hara, *San Francisco Chronicle*
Back Cover Photo: Antoinette Jourard
Interior Design & Typesetting: TBH/Typecast, Inc.
Printing & Binding: McNaughton & Gunn

ISBN 0-918236-05-3

Printed in the United States of America

Published by
FREEPERSON PRESS
455 Ridge Road, Novato, CA 94947

Contents

My First Encounter with Fred

It was during the spring of 1973 that I first encountered Fred. I say "encountered," even though I did not—as you will soon discover—literally meet Fred. He was, in a sense, visited upon me. Because of the extraordinary nature of what I am going to recount, I want, at the beginning, to be precise as to where and when this event took place.

I was then a professor of philosophy at the University of Florida in Gainesville, a middle-sized town set within the sprawling pine forests of northern Florida. I had come to the Department of Philosophy in 1964—originally as chairman—to establish the University's first Ph.D. program in philosophy and to see it through to formal accreditation.

It was a tumultuous period at the University: the war in Viet Nam, draft resistance, student riots, mind-altering drugs, sexual freedom, outdoor rock concerts, and the whole gamut of counter-culture behavior of the hippies and militant radicals. Unfortunately, a large part of that tumult washed over into my department.

In the 1930's, it had been the departments of economics that were politically decried as dangerous havens of radicalism. In the 1940's, the sociologists took their place and were seen as un-American socialistic reformers. In the 1950's, the political science

1

departments inherited this role and were the favorite targets of Senator McCarthy and his committee. Then in the 1960's the heavy mantle fell upon the shoulders of the departments of philosophy—unfortunately for me.

The brightest and most radical students in the University of Florida became philosophy majors, an event that both delighted and dismayed me. It also dismayed the conservative bureaucracy of a Southern state university system that promptly trained all its guns on my once tranquil department and on our all-too-vocal students. Some of our finest students found themselves denounced and threatened by the University's administrators.

Predictably, my faculty soon became incensed at the ongoing persecution of these honorable students, and they too underwent a metamorphosis. Before my eyes, they became radicalized, and they joined cause with the students. Then it was their turn to be denounced by the University's administrators and threatened with dismissal.

And I, caught in the middle of this maelstrom, dutifully defended and protected both my students and my faculty. Although I was successful in doing this, it was, nevertheless, a harrowing ordeal. You can appreciate why. In 1972, with the formal accreditation of the new Ph.D. program now accomplished, I uttered a sigh of relief and relinquished the job of being Chairman to devote myself to teaching. I did not think of it as a retirement, but as a reprieve.

The tumult in my life was not merely academic. I had just been divorced, and a great sadness and rage ached within me. I had the painful sentiment that my life was now irrevocably diminished and, in a sense, tainted. My three children were now unable to relate to me in the old way. The innocence was gone, and a veil seemed to have dropped between us. When we were together, we were now self-conscious. I realized that it would never be the same again, either for them or for me. All of us secretly ached.

At the time I first encountered Fred, two lives had been put behind me—an institutional one and a personal one. I was a bachelor of forty-four, living alone in a brown frame bungalow on the edge of town. Because it was in this house that the first encounter with Fred took place, I will give you the address: 3086 N.W. 14th Street. Last year I went back to see if it was still there. It was. Still sagging a bit, with the screens on the front porch loose and flapping, the bungalow sat there in all its brownness, looking a little like the way I had felt in those days.

There was a woods behind the house—one of the reasons I had rented it—and, about fifty yards into the trees, a spring-fed stream that flowed the year round. The little bungalow with its backdrop of greenery and flowing water was my solace and comfort—a place of retreat. There was a living room, a bedroom, a small bath, and a narrow kitchen. An oil stove, squatting roundly in the middle of the living room, heated the entire house. All in all, it was quite modest, but it was all that I needed.

I do not wish it to appear that I was unhappy, sulking alone in my brown den. On the contrary, I bore my ache quite well and was hugely enjoying myself. My new freedom brought with it a fresh delight in the company of ladies. Three or four times a week, I played handball with Sidney Jourard, my psychologist friend. Outside the bungalow was a motorcycle that took me on idyllic rides through the country roads surrounding Gainesville. In the evenings, there was an abundance of music and food and wine. Half of my friends were eccentric faculty members, the other half were students, and I felt I had the best of both worlds. Because of my highly vocal defense of my department, I enjoyed a modicum of fame in the small world of Gainesville, and this helped smooth out the passage of time as the winter slipped away and the sweetness of spring crept into the peninsula of Florida.

The first Wednesday in May had dawned cool and peaceful. I taught two classes at the University, did some errands, and then returned home for lunch. During the afternoon, I sat outside under the trees and read. It was a lovely, uneventful afternoon.

About five o'clock, I went back into the house and took a shower. After I had dressed, I was puttering about in the kitchen when I heard the screen door of the front porch squeak open, followed by a discreet tapping on the door.

It had already become somewhat dark on the porch. When I opened the door, two young men were standing there. They were typical hippies, wearing blue jeans and T-shirts. I could not make out their faces very well. One was thin and relatively tall; he had a denim jacket over his shirt. The other, standing to his left, was short and compact. Both had long hair that dropped past their shoulders. The tall one was carrying a legal-sized pad under his left arm. Its yellow sheets glowed in the shadows. I had never seen either of them before.

They stood there, silently, looking at me.

I said, "Yes?"

The tall one asked, "Are you Dr. Hanna?"

I told him I was.

He said, "May we come in?"

There was something odd about these two dim figures. I did not sense anything menacing about them, nor did either one give me the sense that he was physically threatening.

I told them they could come in.

Even though it was almost evening, I had not turned on any lamps. The windows of the living room were on the west side of the house, and there was enough late afternoon light to see my two visitors more clearly. The one carrying the yellow pad had a rather gaunt face, accented by a curious darkness around his eyes. He looked haggard, but at the same time he communicated an extraordinary quality of intensity. The shorter one was well-muscled and walked with a light, bouncy spring. His large eyes were dark and shining, dancing with repressed excitement.

"My name is Jean-Baptiste," the tall one said, "and this is Luke." Luke looked at me, smiled, but said nothing. No last names were given, and no hands were shaken. Their formality was awkward. Jean-Baptiste stood there, holding his yellow pad, while Luke gazed at me with mute expectancy.

I motioned toward the couch.

"Would you like to sit down?"

Jean-Baptiste said, "Why don't we just sit here on the rug by the windows?" Young people during that era had taken to sitting on floors, and I had picked up the same habit. We all sat down on the living room floor. Outside, the air was still. Late afternoon shadows fell through the windows and onto the rug, their shapes barely moving.

We sat on the rug, looking at one another. The two young men were certainly not verbose. Jean-Baptiste continued holding the long, yellow pad tucked under his left arm.

I broke the silence. "You said you had a message for me. From whom?"

"From Fred," said Jean-Baptiste.

The only Fred I could think of was an administrator at the University who had just retired. I could not imagine why he would be sending me a message—especially a message borne by two long-haired "freaks."

"Fred Ferguson?" I asked.

"No."

"Then, Fred who?"

"You will see," said Jean-Baptiste. "Here," and he lifted the yellow pad from the crook of his arm and handed it to me.

I took the yellow pad and looked at it. The entire page was covered with handwriting that continued onto the next page. At the top of the first page, it said, "Dear Tom:"

I glanced up at the two of them. Jean-Baptiste waited impassively, seeming almost detached. Luke's large, dark eyes, which were looking directly at me and at the windows behind me, reflected the afternoon sky, framed by the rectangle of the windows.

It was, indeed, a letter, written in black ink. I read it straight through without pausing.

Dear Tom:

Knowing you to be a friend and supporter of good causes, I want to solicit your help. This letter is an introduction to my representative, Jean-Baptiste, whom I have sent to Gainesville to announce the beginning of the New Aquarian Age.

Jean-Baptiste and four of his disciples have come to Gainesville over long distances and at great sacrifice in order to carry out my bidding. They arrive as strangers and are in need of assistance to accomplish their mission. I am certain you will do everything you can to assist them.

In order for them to prepare for the announcement of the New Age, much initial work needs to be done. The time is near, and not a minute is to be spared. During these first weeks, Jean-Baptiste and his disciples will need a place to stay and some material assistance. I know you will be responsive to their needs.

First, I want to request that you invite them to stay at your house – not all of them, of course, since some of the disciples will sleep in the van in which they have arrived. They can park it in back of your house. This arrangement will only be for four weeks while things are being organized.

Second, please offer them a gift of five hundred dollars. It will be of great help. Knowing you to be a man of generosity, I am sure you would have thought of this yourself. The money will, of course, be used only for basic supplies and for publicity.

Third, would you have the kindness to lend them your car during the next four weeks? They will not make use of it all the time, so you will be free to drive it to your classes. At other

times, they will need transportation other than their van to make
all the contacts necessary for preparing the Announcement.

And, fourth, it is essential that you offer Jean-Baptiste full use
of your bathroom whenever he needs it. I expect Jean-Baptiste to
preserve his purity as a holy man, and use of the bathroom is basic.

I appreciate the joy you must feel in helping to launch the
New Aquarian Age right here in Gainesville. Henceforth, Gainesville, like Jerusalem and Mecca, will be known as a place of holy
origins. You yourself will be thrice blessed for being the instrument for spreading this Announcement outward into the world.

Thanking you in advance, I am

Yours,

Fred

When I finished reading, I flipped back to the first page, looking
here and there studiously. What I was really doing was stalling. I
was trying to think of what to say. Four eyes, two somber and two
dark and shining, gazed at me intently, awaiting my response.

After a while, I put down the yellow pad and looked up at Jean-
Baptiste. "There are five of you?"

Jean-Baptiste nodded, "Two women and one other man. They
are downtown, awaiting our return."

"This Announcement," I said, "what is it, exactly, that you are
going to announce?"

"We plan to carry out what Fred has commanded. He has
decided that Gainesville is a place of special enlightenment. The
people here are ready to receive his message. It will be a great
stone dropping into the water: the Announcement received by
Gainesville will expand outward in all directions into the waiting
world. Gradually, more and more of humanity will begin to vibrate
with the ever-spreading message until, eventually, all of humankind is transformed. Then the New Age will begin. Fred has long
awaited this plan's fulfillment, and he has told me that now is the
time for it to begin—and here is the place."

7

"That's . . . that's truly wonderful," I replied, a host of new questions suddenly crowding my mind. "Would you mind telling me something? How was it that you first came in contact with Fred? Did he find you? Or did you find him?"

Upon hearing the question, Jean-Baptiste brought himself erect, his somber gaze fixed just above the top of my head. "You must understand," he said almost in a whisper, "that I was born to be a seeker of the Ultimate."

A passing breeze stirred the shadows on the rug. Luke's eyes had become vortices of swirling light; mirrored there were whorls of tiny leaves dancing airily.

Speaking very quietly, Jean-Baptiste continued. "Seeking the Ultimate is like trying to develop escape velocity to transcend the gravity of the earth. Many others before me have sought Fred, but they did not have enough launch power to reach him. I did. Others have thought that psychedelic drugs were merely for recreation or self-discovery, but, from the beginning, I knew otherwise. I knew that they were the pathway to Fred, and that was why Fred caused them to be invented.

"So I set my mind on achieving contact. LSD was like a launching pad, and I sought that higher realm repeatedly, getting nearer and nearer until one night I finally broke through the barrier. And there was Fred, ready to greet me. I had reached the plane of transcendence where Fred had been patiently waiting for someone to cross over and find him. He had ordained that the first person to cross over the barrier into the Ultimate would become the vehicle for announcing the New Aquarian Age. Since that night of transcendence, he has never ceased to guide and counsel me."

I glanced over at Luke who sat in trancelike rigidity, his eyes fervently locked onto Jean-Baptiste, who now fell silent, his gaunt face looking downward at the shadows on the rug and at the yellow tablet that separated us. I sensed that he was waiting for me to reply to the requests in the letter.

I continued, however, to ask questions. "Are you able to tell me what it is that Fred has in mind? How will this Announcement be made? Is it to be all at once on a given day?"

"Yes," he said, "all at once. Soon, he will disclose to me the precise day when all of Gainesville shall be assembled. Everyone must be there in order for the Announcement to have maximum impact. By the way, do you know of any place that would be large enough?"

I considered the matter. "Well, there is the J. Wayne Reitz Union ballroom on the campus. That is rather large. Then, there is the basketball stadium. It is bigger. At this time of year, the easiest thing would be to have the Announcement out-of-doors."

"But there has to be a stage," he said. "Fred insists."

"That could create a problem. I don't think seventy thousand Gainesvilleans can fit into the J. Wayne Reitz ballroom. There's the football stadium—sometimes they build a stage at one end for special shows. That could be your best bet."

I was trying to be helpful. "But there is something else to consider. Since the five of you are new arrivals in Gainesville, you may find the town a bit different from what you imagine. You are right: there *are* a great number of 'enlightened' people living here— student radicals and thousands of hippies—but remember that northern Florida is located just south of southern Georgia. The local people living around here tend to be extremely conservative. They are called 'crackers,' and they are as tradition-bound as anybody in the South.

"You are going to have a serious communication problem, inasmuch as many of our local crackers might not be able to appreciate the message. It's one problem to get all the Gainesvilleans together in one spot, but it's another problem to get them to understand. In the past, I have had a few difficulties communicating with crackers. Words do not have the same meaning for them as they do for you or me."

9

Jean-Baptiste gave me a gentle, compassionate smile. "Fred is aware of that problem," he said. "And you are quite right: Words cannot communicate the enlightenment of the New Age. A new era requires a new form of communication—one that will cause the scales to fall from their eyes. The Old Age relied on words; the New Age can transcend the old consciousness only by transcending words.

"When I appear and announce the New Age, Fred will make certain that everyone will understand. Every person there, regardless of background, will simultaneously experience the same enlightenment. That is Fred's plan, and that is what will happen."

Fred's plan sounded fascinating. "Exactly what form of communication do you have in mind for seventy thousand crackers and hippies?"

"Dance," he replied. "Fred has bidden me to dance before the multitudes of Gainesville. In this way, there will be no verbal confusion. All will be clear and unsullied. Words are an indirect form of communication, but dance is direct, powerful, and unambiguous."

"Wow!" I said. Then something occurred to me. "Excuse me for asking, Jean-Baptiste, but does that mean you are a dancer?"

"No. I have never danced. That is just the point: it is not I who will dance, but Fred. He will take possession of my body, so that every movement will be his—every gesture will . . . will . . . "

With the last few words, his speech slowed and then, abruptly, Jean-Baptiste ceased talking. His body stiffened and his eyes became fixed. Suddenly, his hand darted into his jacket pocket. I was so startled by the sudden movement that I almost jumped, for it was how someone might reach for a weapon. When his hand re-emerged from the jacket with a ball-point pen, I relaxed.

He paused momentarily, eyes still staring, as if he were listening to distant sounds. Then his left hand reached out and picked up the yellow pad. He placed it in his lap and began writing.

At this point, Luke's body also stiffened, becoming six inches taller, like a soldier suddenly brought to attention. His dark eyes were fixed upon Jean-Baptiste, their orbicular surfaces glistening reverently as he watched his master writing.

Outside, the wind had completely ceased. The silence was a bit unnerving. There was no sound anywhere, either in the house or the woods, except the faint movement of pen against paper. I, too, did not move. Like Luke, I was, somehow, mesmerized, watching the pen go back and forth. The pad in Jean-Baptiste's lap was tilted. I could not see what he was writing.

A slight uneasiness crept over me. I am not easily frightened, but even so, the situation bothered me. I was sitting with two complete strangers, one very certainly schizophrenic and the other a likely candidate; both wanted something from me which I was avoiding giving by asking one question after another. I was becoming apprehensive about where the afternoon might lead.

After a while, Jean-Baptiste finished writing. Even though his hand had come to a standstill, he still continued to stare at the paper as if in a trance. All of us were in a trance. Luke's pupils remained dilated with reverential awe. I was not moving—nor the trees, nor even the air. An ominous stillness lay all about us.

Jean-Baptiste carefully returned the pen to his coat, paused for an instant, then carefully handed me the yellow pad. It was another letter. It read:

Dear Tom:

One of my prime reasons for sending Jean-Baptiste to Gainesville was the large number of wise teachers – such as you yourself – who would instantly recognize the extraordinary importance of this mission.

Only those who already have eyes to see and ears to hear have been chosen by me to help in advancing the New Aquarian Age. These chosen ones will, incidentally, reap the greatest rewards from their efforts.

I greatly regret that persons of wisdom are not adequately recompensed for their remarkable services. Indeed, knowing how difficult it sometimes is to make ends meet on a professor's salary, I suspect that two hundred and fifty dollars will be quite enough to get the mission started.

Also, I want you to know how appreciative I am of the many important activities in which you are involved. Nothing should interfere with that. I can assure you that Jean-Baptiste and his disciples will not at all be in your way. If you have company, they can retire to the van. All in all, Jean-Baptiste only needs the house for press conferences and interviews — only that and, of course, the use of the bathroom.

So, rest at ease on the subject of the house and also the car. Luke knows how to ride a motorcycle, and he can use it to do my work when you need to use the car.

I am sure this clarifies matters. In the hope that this is the case, I remain

Yours,
Fred

I gave the letter a bit of time for reflection. Then I said, "There is something I must tell you: I spent three years studying theology. I was at a divinity school. So you can imagine what a lively interest I have in Fred and his mission. Fred is right: I already have the ears to hear him.

"This does not mean that I am religious. To tell you the truth, I am more or less an atheist. Back then, I was intensely interested in the philosophy of religion. That is why I went to the divinity school.

"For three years, I read about Fred, talked about him — his deeds, his dictums, his laws, and the history of his followers. I became, if you will, a Fredologist. Everything you could want to know about Fred was taught at that school.

"Only one thing was lacking: it was all secondhand knowledge. It had never occurred to any of my professors simply to sit down and write him a letter and wait for a reply. I was given many assignments, but no one was ingenious enough to suggest that I try the direct approach.

"So, you can understand how delighted and appreciative I am that, of all people, it was *I* you chose to visit. It's a wonderful discovery. All those years, I plodded along with nothing but warmed-over theology, never dreaming of anything better. I believed that the only knowledge one could have of Fred was vicarious. I expected nothing more.

"And to think that here, at this very moment and in my own house, I am holding a letter freshly dictated by Fred! I cannot tell you what a revelation this is — actually making direct contact with him. Tell me, Jean-Baptiste, what is it like? What does it feel like to be the medium of Fred's word?"

Jean-Baptiste, who had been slightly slumped over after finishing the letter, now brought his trunk up to a dignified height. He considered my question carefully, making little worried movements with his mouth and jaw. After a moment, he spoke in a quiet voice:

"The greatest event in my life is my relation with Fred. He is my friend and counselor. If I fall, he catches me. If I feel low, he inspires me. If I am confused, he enlightens me. For the first time in my life, I am truly free. I do not have to hold on any more. I can let go, and it is all right, because he is always with me. Right now, I can feel him moving within me . . ."

Then Jean-Baptiste's voice trailed off, his gaze dropping down again. He now seemed to be meditating. Luke and I waited, respectfully silent. The late afternoon stillness had now become a hush. The shadows on the rug had softened, losing their fine edge. As I stared down at the rug, its colors began to pulsate slowly with a soft undulation.

The afternoon was slipping away into evening, and I waited expectantly — almost feeling it in advance — for the coolness that would soon be drifting through my windows. At any moment, it would creep up over the sill, drop down into the room, and flow onto the rug, now slowly pulsing in anticipation of the cool touch of evening.

I bestirred myself. "Jean-Bap*tiste*?" I emphasized the last syllable to get his attention. The haggard young man then looked at me—or, rather, *through* me—his body rigid as a statue and his dark-ringed eyes ablaze with the pink-tinged reflection of the evening sky. Heretofore, he had seemed so mild-mannered, but the strange hardness and intensity of his look caused a sudden chill in my belly and chest.

The catatonic immobility lasted only a moment. He gradually relaxed and refocused his eyes; as he did so, I, too, felt a sense of relief and began to relax a little.

He looked up at me and, surprisingly, smiled. Then he said quietly, "Excuse me. I must have drifted off."

Now that I once again had his attention, I said, "Jean-Baptiste, there is something I want you to know. I fully support your mission. Obviously, you were sent here by Fred to perform an extraordinary deed, and I want to help you in whatever way I can.

"I must confess that when you first gave me Fred's letter, I was doubtful. I was thinking to myself, 'How can I know if he is really communicating with Fred?' Only natural, don't you think? That has passed. I doubt that I am wise, despite Fred's flattering remark. Even so, I usually know the difference between what is authentic and inauthentic. And I can see that it is just as you say it is: you are truly connected to Fred through that yellow pad.

"Now that I have absorbed this wonderful fact, I cannot help but make a proposal to you. Look, here we are—I am a writer, and you are a direct spokesman for Fred. What could be better than for us to collaborate in introducing the New Aquarian Age?

"You obtain the information, and I will write it in a way that everyone can understand—even the crackers. You and I can take Fred's word and give it exactly what it needs: appeal for the mass market. It seems the only way to proceed. It would be the most extraordinary event in the history of publishing. Imagine a series of small readable books answering the major questions about human life; for example, *What Is the Good Life?* Or, *What Is the Best Way to Raise Children?* Or, how about *The Secret of Happiness?* Then there is *How to Stay Healthy,* or *How to Remain Happily Married All One's Life,* or *How to Bring Peace to the World.* There's really no limit to the possibilities. In a sense, the prospects are infinite.

"Can't you imagine the response? The sales? It would be a series of definitive answers to the perennial problems gnawing at the heart of humankind. It would sell like the Bible—indeed, it would be the Bible brought up-to-date. The old Bible had its books, and so will the new Bible, except that its books will be directly relevant to the human condition. The books of our new Bible will be authoritative, last-word treatises on family, health, marriage, love, children, community, and world peace.

"You see the possibilities, don't you? As a publishing duo, we would not only inaugurate the New Aquarian Age, but we could raise millions of dollars to support it and help it spread. I don't think anything could stop us."

While I was saying this, Jean-Baptiste's body began to take on that strange stiffness again, and his eyes became fixed. He had drifted once more into a trance. Moving with great slowness, he reached over and took the yellow pad from me and placed it on his lap. Then he reached into his jacket pocket, took out the pen, and began writing. Luke, who had been somewhat relaxed, came once more to full attention, his eyes glowing like disks of onyx.

The expected coolness now entered the room, falling through the open windows and onto the rug in slow splashes. It was evening—the time of surcease and peace.

When the chilled touch of dusk reached my skin, I became oblivious of Jean-Baptiste and his yellow pad. I was aware only of the shallow pool of coolness in which I sat and of the quietness that engulfed us. My whole being seemed to exude a sigh of relief, and then I, too, dropped into a kind of trance. But this time I felt myself falling haplessly downward into that bittersweet ache which pulsed, like my heart, with a gentle throb. The aching swelled upward from the depths of my being and coiled itself around me. It was an ancient, throbbing feeling, that seemed to be slowly oscillating in phase with the cool undulations of the rug. It was a remote, primal pang of inexpressible disappointment, a systole-diastole of some hurt that was so long ago and so remote as to seem inborn. It was much more than the loss I felt over the divorce and the estrangement from my children. It was much earlier and deeper—a distant, undergirding pain of a remote loss that was as intimate as it was indefinable. It throbbed, ebbing and flowing, like an antiphonal incantation: "The pain is not worth it," followed by the response, "But keep on living." And, again, it intoned, "The pain is not worth it. . . . But keep on living." At my very core, there was something unresolved and aching.

I was lost in a sad reverie when Jean-Baptiste nudged me with the yellow pad.

"There is another letter," he said.

I took the floppy yellow pad and read the third letter:

Dear Tom:

You know, even seventy-five dollars would do wonders. And I am sure all of the other matters can be worked out – the car, the house, even the bathroom. Jean-Baptiste will only need it six times a day. Let us finish with these incidental matters so that we can get on with the real work: inaugurating the New Aquarian Age, in the spirit of which I remain

Yours,
Fred

Jean-Baptiste and Luke waited patiently while I mulled over the third letter. One thing was perplexing me.

"Jean-Baptiste, would you mind telling me about the bathroom? Why do you need my bathroom six times a day?"

"For my purity," he said. "Otherwise, I cannot maintain my holiness. It is the only way I can stay in contact with him. Fred's instructions were explicit."

"But what is it that he explicitly wants you to do in my bathroom—bathe six times a day?"

"No, I am to take six enemas a day."

I was sure I had misunderstood him. "Did you say, 'enemas'?"

"Yes. Six times a day."

This was fascinating. "What kind of enema?"

"Slippery elm," he said. "Those were his instructions."

A car drove up and stopped in my front driveway. Doors slammed. Then I heard the screen door on the porch open. I had the happy presentiment of a rescue party arriving just in the nick of time.

There was a loud knock on the door, and I got up from the rug, went over to the door, and opened it. There stood Barrister, Madman, Scooter, and Chance—student friends of mine. I was overjoyed to see them. They had brought along their guitars, and Barrister was carrying a jug of wine.

I introduced them to Jean-Baptiste and Luke, and soon everyone was sitting on the floor. I fetched glasses from the kitchen while Scooter strummed a few blues chords. Then he began singing a new song by one of our favorite local musicians: a blues singer named Johnny Hines. Johnny's song had a wonderful chorus that repeated the phrase, "It's *all* right! It's *all* right!" It was exactly what I wanted to hear.

I took my own guitar down from the wall and joined in. Soon all five of us were singing "It's *all* right!" which was how I was suddenly feeling. My pleasure with the music was buoyed by the immense relief I experienced at their timely arrival. I had been at my wit's end trying to handle my two visitors. I could not have stalled them forever. "It's *all* right!" I sang. "It's *all* right!" I sensed that I was also singing to the deep ache that had surfaced a few moments earlier.

After a bit, Jean-Baptiste and Luke got up and sat down on the sofa, listening. I ceased thinking about them. When I looked over at the sofa half an hour later, they were both sound asleep.

We played until eight o'clock, when Madman and Barrister announced that they were due at a meeting of the health food cooperative. When they were all about to leave, I asked if they would mind taking along Jean-Baptiste and Luke. Obligingly, they did so. Later, I went out for something to eat. When I came home, I was exhausted and dropped off to sleep instantly.

Late the next morning, I heard some surprising news: Jean-Baptiste had disappeared with the van, leaving his fond disciples behind. Apparently, he had left town for good. The New Aquarian Age was over before it had begun.

Chance, who had met one of the female disciples, phoned to tell me about Jean-Baptiste's departure. When I hung up, I stood in the middle of the living room, musing over the previous night's visit. Out of the corner of my eye, I noticed that they had left something behind. On the big sofa lay the long, yellow pad on which Fred's three letters were written. I put it aside and forgot about it.

The Second Encounter

Years passed before I saw the yellow pad again: eight years—so long that I had forgotten about it completely.

Two years after the incident just recounted, I left Florida and its university and moved to California. San Francisco and Northern California had attracted me like a magnet, and I slipped from Florida's humid grasp.

In California, I continued to teach and perform administrative duties in a graduate school. At one point, I met an old Israeli named Moshe Feldenkrais who possessed almost magical skills in helping people change the muscular system of their bodies—even bodies that were paralyzed or thought to be beyond the pale of help. He taught me some of the things that he did in his work. At an opportune moment I left the academic world and set up a practice in what I called "somatic education." I worked with persons who had medically incurable muscular problems, for I had learned that some so-called "incurable" human disorders could be controlled. Somatic education taught people how to control their bodies.

I had settled in a small town just north of San Francisco. I chose the town for two reasons: it was sunny—just beyond the fogbound communities along the Bay; and it was quiet—something I need as a writer. The office where I practice is only a few minutes from my home, adding further peace of mind. Behind my house is a separate study where I write, surrounded by three walls of books and a tall skeleton that hangs from its stand. When I am not writing something of my own, I am usually busy editing *Somatics*, the magazine which I founded shortly after coming to the West.

Between the study and the main house is a large patio, surrounded by a ring of trees. It affords me great seclusion: no one can see into my arena of greenery, nor can I see out—only up. By good fortune, there is also a creek flowing through the two acres. Unlike the one behind my brown house in Florida, it is not spring-fed, but during the winter, when the rains are frequent, it is a steady stream.

I live at the bottom of a verdant canyon whose tall slopes are festooned with oaks, acacias, manzanitas, and pungently spiced bay trees. The greenery pours its oxygen down to the floor of my little hollow, sweetening the air with its freshness.

There are also some native residents. A family of deer live nearby, and several of their members—usually the younger ones—come to visit me every day. Also, there is a covey of quail near the house, nesting under the gnarled branches of some old plum trees. During the morning, they diligently peck their way through the oat grass and blackberry brambles, the papa quail keeping the covey together with his repeated trumpetings.

Up the hill behind the house is a large rookery of crows whose vigorous cawing announces the early dawn and, just as regularly, foretells the evening as they return noisily from their daily foraging.

I spend much of my summer on the patio, a long slab of concrete which blisters with sunshine during the protracted summer of empty blue skies. In the morning, I often have coffee there, its chilled concrete still shadowed from the early sun. By noontime, the air—always cooled by the nearby Pacific—seems to dance in the sunlight. When I am not working, I usually take off my shirt and sunbathe. By late afternoon, when the shadows return again, the patio is a fine place for reading. When night comes, the sky spreads out its twinkling blackness over the canyon, and an inverted Big Dipper pours its celestial contents down onto the house, the patio, and me.

One bright, early summer afternoon, I was lying on the chaise longue, mulling over my editorial for the next issue of *Somatics*. The sun was a dull red glow under my closed eyelids. Little vermicelli-like squiggles from my inner eye moved across the field of my vision in stately procession.

I was trying to remember a quotation from a medieval philosopher, but I could not recollect the exact words. Frustrated, I got up, walked across the patio into the study, and went over to the bookshelf where I kept a number of volumes on the history of philosophy. They were old books that I rarely had any occasion to use.

My eyes were so sun-dazzled I could not see the books very clearly. After a brief search, I pulled out Volume I of Ueberweg's *History of Philosophy* from the left corner of the shelf against the wood. As I slid the large volume out, instead of seeing the brown of the wood, I saw something yellow—a long, yellow pad. I looked at it, blinking away the sunspots that still swam in my vision. It was sitting up, neatly and flatly pressed between the wood paneling and the Ueberweg book. When I moved in, a friend had helped me unpack my books from Florida. Apparently, the yellow pad had been packed in with the books, and he shelved it by propping it up against the wood so it would not flop over.

Suddenly, eight years were immediately bridged. As I looked at the yellow pad, blinking, I had the uncanny sense of encountering a presence. Its yellow eminence was almost like something alive that had been waiting patiently to be discovered. I was startled. The yellow pad seemed to leap out at me.

For a long moment, I was unaccountably hesitant even to touch it. It sat rigidly upright. At the top was printed, "Efficiency Legal Pad, N. 364-L, 50 Sheets." I reached out and took hold of it from the top and slid it out. There were the three letters of Jean-Baptiste and a pad of empty sheets underneath. I sat at my desk and read through the letters. Then I slowly thumbed through the remaining pages to see if there were any notes inside. There was nothing. The pages were blank.

I left the pad lying on the desk and went back to lie in the sun. I had forgotten about Ueberweg. I lay there, feeling the cool, dry air (so unlike Florida's) and remembering that extraordinary afternoon in my Gainesville living room. I had a clear remembrance of Luke's enormous eyes as they beheld his master writing on the tablet. I was sure that my eyes had been just as wide open.

In retrospect, I realized that Jean-Baptiste had possessed a most special quality in his bearing. There had been a burnt-out dignity in the way he spoke and held his body. The residue of eight years had left me with an amused, almost fond, feeling for those two young hippies of the 'seventies, who had washed up on the shores of my life. I was grateful to them; they had treated me to an unusual experience. Into my uneven, though orderly, mode of academic life, they had introduced two extraordinary novelties: the notion of direct, written communication with the highest being and a relation with this being on a first-name basis. It was the latter that really struck home: "Fred"—the first-name form of address had made the communication so personal. Even now, I realized, I still had a special feeling for someone whom I had come to know as Fred.

Although I had not known it at the time, the two long-haired apostles had given me an acquaintanceship with someone who had an identity, whom I had "met" just as I might encounter any other person. Martin Buber might say that I had been visited with what he called an "I-Thou" relationship.

Lying on the chaise longue, the ruddy squiggles dancing under my lids, it dawned on me that a most special event had happened that quiet afternoon in northern Florida. It was an event that, without my knowledge, had occurred *within* me: namely, I had, as it were, "bonded" with someone named Fred by a kind of internal psychological chemistry. Just as chicks and ducks, on first encounter, bond with the parental presence of the hen or duck, locking onto that being, so had something similar happened to me. Like a duckling, my original "take" on reading that first letter was that a person named Fred had actually sent me a message. That was my mind-set when I first read it. The letters—quite apart from their outrageous content—had seduced me, initially, into accepting the presence and existence of a being who called himself Fred.

I, the shrewd and learned philsopher who harbored profound suspicions of all theological matters, had been accidentally duped into a direct, personal relationship with a being named Fred. I could not deny the fact that I knew a Fred. Worse than that, I could not *un*know him. Lying on the blazing patio, I admitted to myself that I had become unwittingly—I almost wrote "irresistibly"— imprinted with a relationship that I was unable to shake off.

Without even having put in an appearance, Fred had made me, the atheist, recognize him as a person. I had not seen him; nevertheless, I had bonded with him. I realized that it did not at all matter what Fred was saying in the letters—that was irrelevant. The salient point was that, by initially addressing me as a person, he had made me recognize his presence. Once that had happened, I was on the hook. "How tricky!" I thought. "How clever of him!" Then, abruptly, I found myself trying to repress the thought. Aware of my abrupt reaction, I could not help wondering why I felt a need to repress this thought. Was I afraid of someone who did not exist?

When one's eyes are closed, the shape of the sun can still be faintly seen. Through the haze inside my eyelids, I could see, on the yonder side of the squiggles, the sun's round eminence. It glowed dully through my lids. I could not help but remember my first look at Jean-Baptiste and Luke, as they stood in the shadows of my porch. Everything had been obscure and dim — with one exception: the glowing, yellow object. It was right in the middle, cradled under Jean-Baptiste's left arm, with Luke standing on his left.

Even then, it had been obvious: the central event was the glowing, yellow object. That was what had first struck my eyes. Everything had centered in that bright, yellow glow: it was what had brought them there; it was the source of the messages; it was what expanded Luke's eyes to the limit; and now it was the very same yellow glow that was trying to burn its way through the squiggles of my closed eyes. Its brightness would swell and then wane, each time coming back and trying once more to penetrate through my eyelids. I remembered the rhythmical undulations of the rug. I remembered my unresolved ache.

I ceased thinking of anything, simply lying there, aware only of the soft, relentless pulsation of brightness. It moved toward me, then retreated, came toward me again, then retreated. A breeze dropped down onto the patio, stirring the bamboo chimes over the kitchen door. Their hollow, clicking sound added a sound of urgency to the insistent pulsation of the light. I now relapsed into a half-awake state of deep relaxation, floating along with the clicking, rustling pulsation, like a cork floating downriver.

I was no longer experiencing the ruddy, dull glow of the sun. Instead, what I saw was the ruddy obscurity of the porch with Jean-Baptiste and Luke standing there with the yellow pad: they swayed toward me and then away, over and over until, without thinking of what I was doing, I lifted myself up from the chaise and stood up, the breeze catching the perspiration on my back and chilling me awake. Still without thinking, I stumbled across the patio to the study and opened the door. I went directly to the desk and sat down. The yellow pad was lying beneath my hand.

I flipped through the pages of the yellow pad until I came to the blank sheets. I picked up a pen. I confess that the entire event was rather hallucinatory. I could hardly see: the pulsations of light continued, even though my eyelids were open. The pages of the yellow pad glowed brighter, then dimmer, with each pulsation. It was as if the ache were demanding something of me.

What I did next was without the least reflection. I did not think of it as either a lark or a serious act. I did not think at all. It was simply something I had to do. I could not have done otherwise. I wrote at the top of the page:

Dear Fred:
  Are you there?

                    Yours,
                    Tom

There was an interim, an interstice, a time of nothingness, as I mutely watched the waxing and waning of the yellow glow.

Then I felt the back of my pelvis tilt, my right shoulder blade rise, the deltoid contract, and my fingers begin to move.

The pen wrote, and I saw the words spell themselves out in the most natural and unforced manner. Often, a professional writer writes without thinking. That was the way these words were being written; they simply appeared at the end of the pen:

Dear Tom:
  No.

                    Yours,
                    Fred

A Quandary

What had I gotten myself into? After all, this was quite crazy. I picked up the yellow pad and put it right back where it had been hiding between Ueberweg and the wood panel. I decided to forget about it.

But I could not. During the next few days, each time I sat down at my typewriter table, I became acutely aware of its presence. The skeleton, hanging from its steel frame, was directly in front of the table; when I looked straight ahead over the typewriter, my gaze rested squarely in the space between the twelfth rib and the ilium of the pelvis.

For years, I had looked up over the typewriter, seeing only the skeleton. Now, when I looked up, I noticed that the six-inch space in the skeleton was—if I refocused my eyes beyond it—a frame for the contents of the bookcase, a distance of three feet behind the skeleton. Looking through that space, I was amazed to find that I was looking directly at the spot on the bookshelf where the yellow pad was standing. The skeleton was turned in such a way that the rib and the iliac crest were the top and bottom of the frame, and the arm and vertebral column formed the left and right sides. The top of the yellow pad was exactly level with the third lumbar vertebra: the center of gravity for the vertical human body.

Center of gravity? Now I was beginning spontaneously to imagine symbols. It *was* crazy. Yet, I explained to myself, it was not *I* who was making up the symbol, because my chair, table, skeleton, and the yellow pad *did*, indeed, line up. The symbol was self-made.

There was something else bothering me: how could I have been looking directly at the pad for almost eight years without seeing it? That seemed impossible, but the alternative was that during all that time it *wasn't* there until the day I rediscovered it—an option even more unacceptable.

I was unable to work. For three days, each time I sat down at the typewriter, I became acutely aware of the yellow presence in the center of the skeleton. It seemed almost to be watching me.

Well, I thought, all I had to do was take the damned thing off the shelf and throw it away. But, if I did, it would only pull me in deeper: it would mean that I was taking this nonsense seriously, believing that it was something more than a pad of yellow paper. I did not want to do that, so I left it there, trying to defy it.

It was absolutely stupid to play such infantile games with myself. More than stupid. It was easy enough to think of Jean-Baptiste as insane, but now I was considering another possibility: namely, that I myself was beginning to hallucinate and was unable to do anything to stop it.

My first instincts were correct: I had been afraid to touch it and never should have. But *not* to have taken hold of it would also have been attributing too much power to it.

I felt genuinely trapped. It had been been silly to lurch into the study, all dazzled by the sun, and write, "Are you there?" but it was ridiculous to have written a reply to my own question. After all, I had written Fred's reply—with my own hand. I had written it myself. That was true.

It was not as if I were consciously writing. I had written a number of books, and it always surprised me to discover that I never quite knew what I was going to say until I began writing. Once started, the words simply flowed out unconsciously. What had most likely happened was that I had dropped into a writer's frame of mind and written the reply unconsciously.

That was the answer. And I'll admit that I felt a powerful urge to exorcise the whole affair and forget about it, because it was beginning to interfere with my life. Worse, it was causing me to doubt myself. Never before had I entertained the notion that I might be hallucinatory or insane. Now I was spending much of my time entertaining just this possibility.

Another thing: that reply had genuinely surprised me. It was the last thing I had expected to come from the pen. You would think that even though it was written unconsciously, the reply would, in some sense, be an extension of my usual modes of thinking. When that "No" came out, it was almost like a blow. It was totally unexpected, and it hit me unprepared in exactly the same way as if someone had answered the question from a completely different frame of reference. It was just one word, that reply, but it was the last word I could have imagined.

A letter from Fred? It was a joke—a crazy joke I was playing on myself. It is all very well to read of prophets and holy men who claimed that God talked to them, but that was thousands of years ago and not the 1980's. Besides that, no one called *God* "spoke" to them—that was merely the way in which the priestly writers of those ancient texts expressed it in order to give authority to their holy writ. It was hokum then, and it was hokum now—my own self-induced hokum.

The religious citizen is not at all disturbed when he hears, in the Sunday sermon, that "God spake unto Abraham"; but when church is over and he walks out on the street, if some fellow were to approach him and say, "God told me to speak to you," that citizen would forthwith call a cop. Why? Because the sane citizen, despite his churchly attendance, never takes such things seriously. Without even reflecting on it, he takes stories of God's communication figuratively, but never literally. If he does take such things literally and seriously, he, too, will be considered insane.

So here I was, haunted by that yellow pad and what was written on it. It wasn't the Bible or the Bhagavad-Gita, and it wasn't thousands of years ago. It was a perfectly ordinary legal pad, and it was right now. And I, like a perfect idiot, was taking the whole matter literally and seriously.

It was too much. I was treading strange waters and did not know how to get out. Far worse, I wondered if, deep down, I really *wanted* to get out. Perhaps, at some obscure level, I fancied that a being named Fred really had chosen to write to me—picked me out, so to speak. Me, above all others. All things considered, it was dizzying to think that if such a thing were possible, it was happening to me—a truly astonishing, miraculous event.

But I always wheeled back to the unavoidable conclusion that if I really did believe this was happening, then I was as mad as a hatter. Maybe I *was.* Everyone back East thought that if you are a bona fide nut, you will be ineluctably drawn to California. And here I was, drawn to just this place as by a magnet. After breathing the California air for eight years, was I beginning to lose my bearings?

What if I did believe that Fred was communicating with me? Then what? If I were crazy enough to pick up that yellow pad and write another letter to Fred and if I were to get a reply from him, what would I do about it? For one thing, I could not tell a soul. I would have to shut up about it and keep it secret. To do otherwise would be disastrous, for I would be considered a laughing stock.

But, if I kept it a secret, what would finally come of it? Here would be good, old Tom Hanna, writing his books and treating his clients in a perfectly sane manner—then stealthily entering his study at night, drawing the curtains, and holding converse with an unseen being named Fred. What would come of it is psychosis. I knew that. One would have to be two irreconcilable personalities in order to do that. From what I knew about schizophrenia, in the long run it would no longer be a secret. The dual existence would eventually break down, and everyone would say, "Too bad about Tom. Who would have thought it?" I would be promptly shipped off to the funny farm.

For three days I did nothing but thrash about in my predicament. I could not work, so I ate, slept, and lay in the sun. It was like being in a fever. A peculiar soul sickness had taken possession of me, and everything that was healthy and balanced and sane seemed to be slipping away. I was wavering. Each day I lay there on the patio, surrounded by oaks and acacia trees blowing in the young summer winds, contemplating that dull glow of the sun behind my eyelids—and, always, there it was: the yellow pad. It was pulsing: Fred came toward me, trying to enter, and then, hitting resistance within me, faded back, only to come again.

I knew that I could not go on like this—feverishly wavering. Otherwise, I would surely become sicker. I had to get rid of Fred— or let that presence come in. It had become increasingly clear to me that the first option was not going to happen: I could not get rid of him. He had become an obsession. But if I let him in . . . well, thinking of the consequences caused me to feel infinitely sad. And also frightened. I did not wish to go insane, yet it was beginning to appear that there was no other direction in which to go. Then again, perhaps it was only by choosing to give in to Fred that I could exorcise him. This was madness! How could I lie there, rationally—or at least semirationally—deciding whether or not to go insane? Could you *decide* to go insane? Was I wavering before the "great leap of faith" that Kierkegaard had talked about, when you embraced the absurd, forsook the world, and fell weeping and drooling in the arms of God? I did not at all want that. It would be the end of my life as I knew it. Indeed, it would mean the end of me.

What if I *did* become a schizophrenic? Perhaps schizophrenia *is* the higher, transcendent reality that all humans yearn for, but are too afraid to leap into. Isn't the sanity of ordinary consciousness the sign of an ordinary life, a life of cowardice and nonachievement? Is that what I was, a coward? Why should I allow the ordinary logic and rationality so prized by philosophers to rob me of an extraordinary discovery about life and its ultimate roots?

Whom was I trying to protect—myself or the inane traditions of philosophy? Wasn't all this wavering the symptom of my inability, or my unwillingness, to free myself from strictures that were holding me back? Fred was, quite possibly, reaching out to me, offering transcendent knowledge; and I, a "lover of wisdom," was acting like a quivering poltroon, holding back, afraid to face truth, and hiding behind the intellectual snobbery of atheism.

On the afternoon of the third day, the wavering finally ceased, and a settled resolve somehow took its place. The feverish vacillation was over, and a strange, calm lucidity now took possession of me. I arose from my patio sickbed and went into the house, where I shaved, showered, and then crawled into bed. I was exhausted.

But I was happy. For reasons I could not clearly fathom, I had decided to let Fred in.

A Short Inning

It was a troubled sleep. Most of the night and well into the next morning, I stayed on a fine edge between dreaming and conscious thought.

I was in a feverish reverie, as if I were still outside on the patio, perspiring, fidgeting, and helplessly pinned down by a relentless light that repeatedly bore down upon me. Countless times, I reacted by getting up and, dripping with perspiration, walking across the patio and into the study. But now, in my hectic dream, it was too dark in the study. I could not clear the bright light from my eyes; in the darkness, it hovered in front of me fantastically, like a glowing, yellow pad. I would reach out for the yellow phantasm, touching only air. Nothing was there—but the indistinct blur remained, tantalizing me to reach out again as it retreated from my grasp.

It was vitally important that I seize the yellow pad and reestablish contact with Fred, but the luminous pad continually eluded my efforts. It was like a great, yellow butterfly slowly moving about the room with languorous flaps of its wings. Each time that I tried to grasp it, it fluttered just beyond the reach of my fingertips.

I remained all night in this half-lit, fluttering uncertainty, reaching repeatedly for the yellow glow that forever evaded me. The salt of perspiration seeped down into my eyes, stinging them and blurring my vision even more. It was not until just after dawn and the sound of the awakening crows that I fell into a deep and dreamless sleep.

I awoke at noon, feeling tired and a bit clammy. Again, I showered and shaved. That helped. Then I improved matters further by making a cup of mint tea. I hunched over it, inhaling the vapors. My mind gradually became lucid, and the fragrance of the mint seemed to cleanse me of the night's troubled reverie.

I sat at the table, waiting until the right moment to get up and do what was now inevitable: to go into the study and write to Fred. This time, my choice of words had to be exactly right—no carelessness in the phrasing. I had been thoughtless when I had asked him that first question, and that was why he had answered as he did. But this time, I was going to be sure that my thoughts were clear, so that I could choose my words wisely.

I began thinking of last night's feverish dream. Could it have been an omen? My inability to reach the fleeing yellow pad—was that a premonition? Perhaps that very first question—so careless and thoughtless—had already destroyed my one chance of communication with Fred. Perhaps one question was all I was going to get, and the adventure was already over.

Had my miserable wavering during the past three days been for naught? Was the strange feverishness only a self-inflicted punishment for having offended him and lost him? There was every probability, it seemed, that I had had my chance and muffed it. Last night's dream might have been my way of telling myself that the communication was terminated and the privilege withdrawn.

Whatever the case, I had to find out. I rinsed the cup, walked out the kitchen door, crossed the patio, and entered the study. It seemed unusually bright and cool inside. I took the yellow pad from the shelf and sat down at the desk. I spent a moment to gather my thoughts; then I picked up the pen and carefully wrote:

Dear Fred:
Forgive me. I simply want to know you.
                    Yours,
                    Tom

This time, there was no pause whatsoever. I saw my hand drop down three lines on the yellow paper, move over to the left margin, and the following words appeared:

Dear Tom:

How human! How nauseatingly human! There have been only four words exchanged between us, and You are already down on your knees begging forgiveness. Is this any way to start a relationship – by humiliating Yourself?

Do You really believe that such abject behavior impresses me? Do You think that I have the least interest in seeing You – or anyone – bowing, kowtowing, kneeling, davening, groveling, and prostrating? I do not. It is not only ludicrous, it is hell on the knees. If You had been truly careful and thoughtful in approaching me, You might have started off by standing up like a man and trying to look at me with a level gaze.

But You have gone beyond being merely ludicrous. On top of that, You want me to forgive You. How utterly outrageous! Why in the world do you think I should forgive You? Both of us know the answer to that: You think I must have judged You. Right? But where did You get the lame-brained idea that I have judged You? Or that I have the slightest inclination to judge You? Do You have any idea how presumptuous it is to accuse me of being a judge? That really irks me.

You say You "simply want to know me." That is pure poppycock. To the contrary, it is obvious You think You know me already: first, You allege that I am a judge; second, You allege that I have judged You; and third, You have the gall to tell me to forgive You. That seems like a lot of prior knowledge for someone who pretends he does not even know me.

It is not knowledge You are displaying. There is a different word for it: insolence. You are the one who seems to be omniscient – not me. We have not even shaken hands yet, and already You are glibly instructing me as to who I am and what I am supposed to do.

Let me tell You, right off the bat, that at this stage in my career, I have not the least desire to take instructions from some chaise-longue Moses feverishly brandishing a yellow tablet of the law.

I want to make something indelibly clear to You, Thomas: I am not who You think I am. *Please keep that in mind.*

So then, let me summarize: first, You know nothing about me; second, You have no reason to accuse me of being a judge; and third, I simply detest people who grovel.

That is three strikes. You're out.

The inning is over.

Yours,
Fred

Logical Reflections on the Revolving Door

Well, at least we had communicated—even though not very satisfactorily. My attempt to approach Fred "thoughtfully" and "carefully" was a bust. There was no way of knowing how to approach him—or even how to address him. I had originally come to know an individual named Fred, so it was natural for me to address him as "you" rather than "You." But then he turns this around another one hundred and eighty degrees by addressing me as "You." It made no sense.

What was I supposed to do now? Despair of the entire situation and throw myself on his mercy? But I already knew that such a traditional approach would not work. He would not tolerate it. He would say I was begging forgiveness, and then throw the whole thing back in my face. Approaching Fred was like going into a revolving door, spinning around, and going right back out again.

Certainly, I could understand what he meant when he said that I was *expecting* him to judge me. He was right: at the very moment I was asking to know him, I had already assumed, *a priori*, that he was judging me. Yes, I *was* presumptuous. He really had me on that one. I was acting as if I were the one who was omniscient.

O.K., but even if he were not exactly judging me, he did admit he was "irked" with me. I was irksome, because I had preconceived notions about him. Of course, I could blame all this on my years of theological education. It had stuffed my head with so many preconceptions I would never weed them out, no matter how thoughtful and careful I tried to be.

It was strange that I should revert to my old theological learnings when I had never believed any of it in the first place! I was an atheist; in theory, I should have no preconceived notions of any kind about him.

But hold on: presumably, I was now officially an *ex*-atheist, since it does not really make sense that an atheist could be involved in this kind of correspondence. Even so, I did not think that this made me a "believer."

It would be incorrect to say that I "believed" in Fred. It had not happened that way. I had, on one fine summer day, encountered him. He was "visited upon me." Belief had nothing to do with the situation. I might encounter the President and make his acquaintance, but that would not mean that I *believed* in him.

It was absurd. How could an atheist—a nonbeliever—hold converse with the Almighty? It seemed to me that it is only when you do not have direct acquaintance that you have to resort to the second-level activity of believing. And, since I had direct acquaintance, I did not need to believe.

I was, I supposed, still an atheist, not only because I disbelieved in theology but also because I did not *believe* in him. Instead, I *knew* him. It was *theology* that Thomas doubted, not the *theos*.

But there it was: three strikes, and I was out. I was out the revolving door. I had swung and missed three times—missed by a mile. As a result, I was now clearer of mind—and of heart. I had been irksome. O.K., but I could forgive myself for it. It was not Fred's job to forgive me.

I was clearer about another matter: even though I had met Fred on a prior occasion, that did not at all mean that I really "knew" him. On the contrary, it had suddenly become obvious that I knew absolutely nothing about him. That was why he was pressing the point that he was not who I thought he was. The entire battery of my theological knowledge had nothing to do with him.

I dimly perceived that what really irked Fred—my personal shortcoming—was that I was not *enough* of an atheist and that I had presumed to know him other than through direct acquaintance. What I knew came from reading theology and listening to sermons.

This meant that Fred did not believe in theology any more than I did. What was irksome about me was that I had backslid away from my atheism. He was upbraiding me for not being pure in my disbelief.

So, the conclusion was as obvious as it was unfathomable: Fred was an atheist.

A Few Questions

Now, having learned my lesson, I revised my strategy. No matter how "thoughtfully" and "carefully" I approached Fred, any approach was foredestined to be the wrong. Any presumption was automatically a wrong assumption. I concluded, therefore, that the best approach was no approach.

Since it was now a certainty that I really did not know anything about Fred, the only recourse was to address him empty-handed and empty-headed, like an innocent—which, admittedly, I was. I must stand before Fred as a virgin: ignorant, not knowing what to expect, not knowing what to ask, not daring to reach out. I must become passive and expectant, calling his name and then waiting.

These were the thoughts flitting through my mind while I paced the length of the study, slowly moving pendulumlike back and forth in front of my desk on which the long, yellow pad was lying. A half-hour had gone by since the end of the last letter. I had licked my wounds and regrouped my forces. Now I felt ready.

I waited for the moment when everything felt just right, and at that point I stopped pacing. I faced the yellow pad and stood very still for a moment. Then I sat down and wrote the following words:

Dear Fred:
   I want to know you.

                        Yours,
                        Tom

I brought my hand down three lines and waited, pen poised. A minute passed. Nothing happened. I waited, the pen poised and ready. Three minutes went by.

My shoulder and wrist began to ache. I noticed that I was holding my breath. I looked up at the clock and decided to wait five more minutes. I closed my eyes and breathed slowly and deeply. As time continued to pass, I felt tendrils of despair growing within me. I opened my eyes and looked at the clock: six minutes had passed.

It was not going to happen. The communication had ended. I sighed, lowered the pen, and felt my shoulders drop.

Immediately, my hand was drawn to the left margin of the page, and my fingers began to write.

Dear Tom:

Sorry to make You wait, but virgins must realize they not only do not know what to expect, but they do not know when to expect it. By the way, I trust You are not laboring under the old illusion that by pressing Your pen to the yellow pad You obligate me to speak. Spare me that one. Rituals have never obligated me to do anything.

But that is a side issue. What is important is that I liked Your letter: short and to the point. In a word, pithy. So, You want to know me? That is a decided improvement over groveling in the dust and abjectedly claiming You "simply" wanted to know me. You may quickly discover that getting to know me is not at all a simple matter. Worse, You may, on closer acquaintance, decide You really do not want to know me – that You have bitten off more than You care to chew.

So, Tom, where shall we begin? How should I introduce myself? You already know my name, so that is behind us. What else would You like to know? My age? What I look like? Where I live? Where I was born? What I prefer for breakfast? What's my favorite color? Isn't that how one becomes acquainted?

You may wish to know what I do for a living? Am I gainfully employed? Or, how many hours do I put in each day? Do I get tired? Bored? What do I do with my leisure time? Do I like sports? Do I play games? Am I any good at chess and billiards? Would that help You come to know me?

What is it that You really want to know? There are endless questions. Perhaps You want to know about my sex life. Whether I prefer women or men? Or both? Or whether Fred is short for Frederica, and I am a woman? How does that set with You? Or how will You react if I tell You I am hermaphroditic — as womanly as I am manly? Will that cause You to have uncomfortable feelings about me? Perhaps a hint of disgust?

What I am asking is whether You are quite certain that You want to find out about me. I say this because once You know, You will not be able to forget. You will be stuck with this knowledge the rest of Your life.

No, I'm not teasing You — it is not my nature to mock man. But You can appreciate, I'm sure, that getting acquainted with me is not a matter of asking ordinary questions. My age, occupation, and sex are somehow irrelevant, aren't they? Somehow, the ordinary questions sound ridiculous. Well, then, what other kinds of questions are there for You to ask? In general, the only way You come to know a person is with ordinary questions. But if such questions do not reveal who I am, then how will You ever come to know me? Maybe it is an impossible task.

The very first question You asked me was, "Are you there?" I replied, "No," which was correct. Why didn't You ask, "Are you here?" That would not have made much sense, would it? Because if I were already "here," You would not need to ask me if I were here. Or would You? You might very well have asked me, "Are you here and there?" but You wouldn't have bothered asking such a nonsensical question. Actually, I should have replied to Your first question by saying, "Dear Tom: Are You there?"

Inasmuch as each stage of our brief correspondence has left You wracked with soul-searching doubts, that reply would certainly have got Your full attention. And rightly so, I think, because men are so concerned about the question, "Does God exist?" that it never occurs to them that I may be equally concerned with the parallel question, "Does man exist?" There are millions of You running around looking very much like human beings, but the serious question is whether human beings are really there?

While You worry about the possibility of God, I worry about the possibility of man. Every day I ask myself, "Does man exist?" Or is humankind only a figment of my imagination? A mere belief. Most of the time, my temptation is to pass it off as that—as a mere fantasy of mine. I cannot help wondering if I am deluding myself—hoisted on my own anthropological petard.

When I view humankind, am I the victim of my own projections? Observing You is like listening to a bad short-wave transmission that fades in and out. At times, I think I am hearing a human, but the sound is so unclear and distant I am never quite sure. Just at the instant that I begin to make out a human voice, it becomes garbled and fades away into nothingness, and I am left wondering if I really heard a human or only believed I did.

In that regard, I am a bit like You: I do not want to "believe" in man, taking it on faith that man exists. That is not enough. I want to know that man exists. I want to see what is human, hear what is human, feel it, touch it, taste it, smell it. Why should I settle for second best?

I'm sorry. Here I am talking about anthropos, *and You want me to talk about* theos. *Forgive me. Anthropology is a kind of obsession with me, just as theology is with You.*

So where are we? Yes, we were asking ordinary questions and noticing how funny they sounded. Things like, do I really rest on Saturday, or is it Sunday? That's a good one. Or, even better, do I get any rest at all? Or, as they used to say back in the eighteenth century, am I on a permanent vacation now that I have created the clockwork of the world, wound it up, and set it ticking? The deists figured I had retired and been put out to pasture.

Well, there You jolly well have it: ordinary questions will get us nowhere. If You wish to know me, there is no option but to ask extraordinary questions. Which is no easy matter, since I cannot see any limit to how many extraordinary questions can be asked. Indeed, if I am not who You think I am, then it follows that I may be anything You think I am not. That leaves a colossal number of possibilities.

I might, for example, be Everything. What do You think of that possibility? Or I might very well be Nothing. That option has a certain vogue.

Would You like it if I were All and Nothing? Would that be inclusive enough to satisfy You? Then, again, I may not be the All so much as a Certain Quality of the All.

If that does not ring Your bell, perhaps You can think of me as the Structure-of-All-That-Is.

Or as the Form-of-Forms?

We could certainly try the Unmoved Mover, but that's out of style now.

You might try another tack and think of me as the Process-of-All-That-Is. At least, that gets us out of the Platonic rut.

For the sake of completeness, we might try: the Structure-and-Process-of-All-That-Is: Plato sitting in Whitehead's lap.

Want more? I might be none of the above. I might, instead, have the principled status of being the Law-of-the-Cosmic-Process. That sounds reassuringly legal, if that is Your bent.

Or am I the Creator with a long white beard, sitting on his throne? That's old-fashioned, but still popular.

Or give it a twist: Am I the Creating?

The options are far from exhausted. Am I, perhaps, the Victim-of-a-Process-Not-of-My-Own-Creating?

Everyone of these are extraordinary questions, all of which may be true and all of which may be false.

But, my dear Thomas, I have saved for the last the most extraordinary question of all: isn't it possible that I do not know the answers to all these questions?

Yours,

Fred

I sat at the desk, gazing at the yellow pad and feeling a bit frustrated. I flipped the page back and read the letter once again. I had not asked him a question—that was my new strategy: I had simply addressed him with a noninterrogatory statement. And what had I received in response? Questions.

Getting to know Fred was no easy matter. If anything, I now knew less about him than before. It was almost as if he were waltzing around, evading me. Even though I had no intention of asking it, I had now begun to entertain a new question: is it possible that God is a wag?

A Drive
to the City

The following day, I had some errands to do in San Francisco. I clambered up into the old Volkswagen van; as I was backing it out of the driveway, I saw two deer standing over in my side yard. They stood motionless, watching me, their ears held high.

The meandering country road that takes me into town is covered over with huge oak trees where it passes by my house. I drove under its canopy down to the bottom of the road, and then turned a sharp right where Joanie's horse ranch begins. The sloping pastures were dotted here and there with grazing horses, and the big pond was busy with ducks paddling about in tiny armadas. The winding road ended when I reached Hill Street. I turned twice more, and then went straight through town to the highway that leads southward to the city.

It was a clear, brilliant day. Sunlight seemed to well up from the rolling landscape. Summer days in the wine country of Northern California are hypnotically repetitive: totally clear skies each and every day. In April, the dark rains of wintertime cease to fall, and for the next six months—lasting into October—the skies are pristine. Wine country weather: dry, clear days that are rarely too hot and cool, clear nights that are sometimes too cool.

My little town is at the lower border of the wine country, a region that stretches northward into the counties of Napa,

Sonoma, and Mendocino. Just off the highway to my right I could see the private vineyard that one of my neighbors had planted. An acre of grapes sprawled alongside his white Victorian house. Soft, green leaves covered the tiny grape clusters just beginning their long, patient progress toward autumnal plumpness.

I threaded my way through the rounded contours of Marin County, whose skin-smooth hills were dry and tawny. The wild oats covering the hills now lay parched under the rainless skies.

The undulations of the landscape were surprisingly sensual, the curves so smooth that the earth seemed in the process of heaving its mass upward into the shapes of breasts and buttocks, cheeks and shoulders: an incarnated landscape. I lifted my left hand in front of my face and held it in a grasping position. Then I looked through the hand at the earth's body and pretended to squeeze a buttock here, tweak a nose there, and caress a breast in the distance. It made for an interesting drive.

By the time I was halfway to the city, something ominous appeared on the horizon. As I looked southward toward the Golden Gate, the flashing gold of the smooth hills gradually dulled, became darker, and at the edge of the horizon were swallowed up into a wintry gloom. It was the summer fog, whose misty tongue licked at the bright hills, seeking to draw them into its maw.

It was a strange scene, created by the meeting of the cold, moist ocean air and the dry, hot desert air of California's inner valleys. I understood what caused the phenomenon; even so, it gave me an uneasy feeling. The city toward which I was heading seemed a dark entity, reaching out and engulfing the glowing flesh of the living earth. I thought of the dark holes at the center of the starry constellations, sucking matter into their voracious emptiness.

When I reached the Golden Gate Bridge, I entered the black hole. Abruptly, it became chilly and dark. I had to roll up the window. It made me feel terribly far away from my deer and quail and crows. I felt far from Fred.

When the Buddha sought enlightenment, he went into the searing heat. Mohammed found Allah in the desert. John the Baptist looked for God in the same desert heat. Jesus spent forty days and forty nights in the wilderness of the Sinai desert and returned transformed by God the Father.

It was not in the city that Fred was to be found, but only in the clear desert air—the dry, hot air of my country retreat. The place to seek enlightenment was not in the density and darkness of the city, but in the loneliness and light of open space.

I drove into the dark embrace of one of the world's most beautiful cities, feeling progressively estranged from Fred. It was as if I were running away from him. I thought of Fred and sunlight, and I realized that the glowing, yellow pad had, from the very beginning, been a harbinger of the desert light from which Fred had appeared with his many questions.

Cities have answers for many things. They are founded upon answers and certainties. They represent closure—decisions that humans have reached in answer to their problems. As I drove through the cool urban darkness, so filled with answers and solutions, I was yearning for a warm brightness filled with questions.

Eggs

The next day was Sunday, and I awoke thinking of Fred's letter. I was regretful that it had ended so soon.

At first, the letter seemed to be moving toward a grand revelation, as if the heavens were trembling and about to open. What was so electrifying was that it was not at all a "revelation" in the traditional sense; rather, it was the beginning of a self-revelation. But, strangely, it progressed without revealing anything at all.

Fred made as if to open his great cloak, but then he abruptly swirled it shut again. Even so, I realized that something had been communicated: although nothing was revealed, his fingers had strummed a long arpeggio across the strings of an immense harp; against the background of his abrupt cessation, the cascade of notes lay still shimmmering upon the silence.

I wanted more. I was now "hooked," unashamedly thirsting after the possibility of divine revelation. How ironical for me, the presumed atheist and skeptic. I suppose that was what I still was, but it seemed now that I was in the ludicrous position of being an atheistic skeptic thirsting after Fred's revelation.

The skeptic in me was still there, telling me that what was really going on was a pathetic act of self-delusion—that I was enmeshed in a pathological state of mind wherein I was writing to myself while projecting the action on somebody else: Fred.

But, I reasoned, if I really *were* a conduit for Fred's word, it would be no different: it would still be *I* who was doing the writing, and the event was unquestionably taking place in *my* brain and *my* hand; thus, it would always be possible to look at the event skeptically, if I chose to do so. I could play it either way—as believer or skeptic—but the phenomenon itself would nonetheless be the same: it was the experience of being the vehicle for someone else's thoughts.

Who was I to deny the reality of what I myself experienced? Of course, I wanted it to continue—whatever was happening. Admittedly, it was crazy, but I was damned if I was going to stop it.

But what was my next move? Whether real or delusional, I was gripped by excitement at the possibility of another letter, of another opening of that cloak—perhaps wider this time. I was also aware how delicate the situation was. Whatever was going on, I could not afford to be thoughtless or careless in my approach, for the reality or delusion might abruptly cease. I would have to proceed with caution.

Those were my reflections on that early Sunday morning. They continued through breakfast. They continued as I sat on the patio with a second cup of coffee, and they grew more intense when I went into the study. There it was, waiting for me: the pad with its yellow aura.

As I looked down at the yellow pad I felt pulled toward it— literally compelled to write to Fred. But compelled to write *what*? I knew Fred was expecting some kind of response from me, but I did not have the foggiest idea of what to write.

It was almost a repetition of the impulsive manner in which I had written the first letter to Fred: I sat down, took up the pen, and wrote the truth:

Dear Fred:
  I do not know what you expect of me.
                    Yours,
                    Tom

For a long instant, there was a hiatus—an experience of absolute silence and emptiness. Then I felt a subtle lurching of my right shoulder blade. A soft force coursed from my shoulder, down the arm, and then into the fingers. The pen dropped down and wrote:

Dear Tom:

Good. Very good. You are quite right: it was Your chess move. I was wondering if You might open with the Ruy Lopez or maybe the Pillsbury Attack. But You chose the Giuoco Piano opening: the perfect move to draw me out.

You say that You do not know what I expect of You. Fair enough. Since virgins do not know the ground rules, they are not supposed to know what is expected of them. So what should You do but be honest? I like that. You showed good taste in realizing that whatever it was I expected, at the very least I expected You to be honest about Your confusion. By the bye, I commend You for something else: being honest about Your skepticism. That adds a certain piquancy to what we are doing.

Allow me to make a résumé of the situation: You want to know me, but You do not know how to go about it. You would like to ask questions, but You don't know which questions to ask — certainly not ordinary ones. I think we are clear about that. But which of the extraordinary questions should You ask? I offered only a hint of the kind of questions You might ask, but that arpeggio — as You so sonorously named it — was, I should think, enough to suggest the rest of the symphony. After all, why recite an epic poem when a haiku will do as well?

The arpeggio had a useful musical function: it gave You a scale with which to attune Yourself. Knowing me will — at the very least — require You to enlarge the range of Your hearing. You will want to be as sensitive to the tinkle of the highest frequencies as You are to the diapason of the deepest range.

More than that, You will want to appreciate the most delicate pianissimo just as much as the most powerful onslaught of decibels.

The arpeggio of questions was a tune-up to help You adjust Your ear, so that I could communicate with You. I am sure You realize that the only way to open oneself up is by asking questions. To ask questions is to reach out, to seek. Answers do the reverse: they close down; they do not dispose one to learning. Isn't that what was on Your mind when You drove into the city? When it comes to extraordinary matters, answers are quite inappropriate. They are dead and useless. Questions, on the contrary, are bristling with freshness and life. They are the fingers of growth.

There is no other course: if You want to know me, You must expand the height and width and depth of Your sensitivity – not just Your hearing but also Your range of vision – to all shades of color from the glowing edge of the infrared to the deep intensity of the ultraviolet frequencies. Your eye must be quick to descry all possible shapes and lines and contrasts.

You must open up Your sense of smell – not being afraid of what You think You might not like, nor being restrictive by defining in advance and for all time what You like and do not like.

It is the same for Your taste. How many tastes are there? How broad is the palette of Your palate? Have You already circumscribed the limit of what is palatable, or are You still open to adventures? A famous cheese would never have been discovered had the first man to see that green-veined putrescence been afraid to taste what he had found in the cave at Roquefort.

You must allow Your skin its full reign. Skin is not only for protecting and shutting you off from the world; it is for touching and caressing the world – reaching out to the environment, opening to take it in its vibrations, heat, light, and moisture.

Let Your pores open: they are a million tiny mouths with which to drink in the world.

Most of all, You must expand Your sensitivity to Yourself and to Your inner flow — to the ceaseless flood that engulfs Your awareness and carries You along into newness. You must sense the hesitations and surges, the strange blendings and concatenations of feelings — the preparations, the leaps, and the sudden halts of Your inner universe.

In fine, if You want to know me, You must get in shape to do so. You must learn to experience Yourself for what You are: living, moving, and unresolved.

You are a living question: every breath You take and every moment You live is a question. You must learn to recognize Your incompleteness, Your constant inconstancy. You must face up to the truth that nothing about You is fixed or final or defined.

I do not want this to sound offensive, Tom, but, in a precise sense, You are nothing. Ultimately, You are not anything at all. If You were something, You would be dead: You would be an answer.

Does this help You appreciate the rationale behind my arpeggio of questions? It was intended to stir the same questioning vibrations within You. Otherwise, You will not be able to perceive me. To "know" me is not to understand me; You have to sense me. Otherwise, how will You know where I am?

Remember, You asked, "Fred, are you there?" Yes, to a certain extent I am "there"; however, that answer is not fully correct, since I also happen to be "here."

That is a fundamental question: where is "here"? At this point, You can fairly well guess the answer to that: "here" is You. "Here" is Your centrum: if You cannot fully sense what is happening in Your centrum, You cannot know where "here" is.

I trust You get my point. Obviously, I am both "here" and "there"; otherwise, I could not be who I am. But most humans find it impossible to think of me as both "here" and "there." Many people – especially during the present century – have become quite skillful at perceiving what is "there." Many others – and they have become scarcer this century – are experts in sensing what is "here." Few humans know – or even care to know – how to experience where both "there" and "here" are.

You say You do not know what I expect of You. Fair enough. However, give Yourself credit. No communication is possible without honesty, and You know that is a fundamental expectation. Now I am suggesting that You must be able to tune into all the frequencies in which I communicate – and those frequencies are both "here" and "there."

As a teacher, Professor Hanna, You know very well that genuine teaching involves more than just giving information. The teacher must create the conditions which enable the student to understand what is communicated. You, then, are the student seeking to know me, and I am the teacher concerned about Your ability to understand what is communicated.

It is not so much what I expect of You as what is demanded by the situation itself. It is an honesty that is total – where You admit to Yourself that Your being is always incomplete and flowing. That is the way one recognizes his Hereness.

However, allow me to push the point a tiny bit further. What the situation demands is, finally, this: You must hatch Yourself.

There, I have said it. It is what You were waiting for. But it is not very clear, is it? So, I will explain. It's like this: Your body once lay sleeping within the warm embrace of an egg. That was during Phase One of Your life – the foetal stage: the dream time when You were flesh of flesh, cell within cell.

Then came Phase Two when You were hatched from the egg and became fully exposed to the "Thereness" of the world. Your bodily "thereness" did not come into existence until You left the nurturing protection of the egg and became exposed to the world and all its forces.

It is obvious that human bodies have these two stages of growth: the foetal and the postnatal. It is less obvious that Your soul has these same two phases. As soon as You have left the foetal stage and entered the world, You need something just as important as a body. You need a persona. *But You are not born with a persona — only a body. So how do You acquire a persona?*

That is an easy one. You acquire it from Your family. The family is the womb which nurtures the first persona, providing it with information as to what that persona can do, what it needs, what its hopes should be, and what its world is all about. The nest of the family provides the infant human with the straw, filaments, and fibers to thatch a persona.

In the center of the nest are the mother and father upon whose nurture and protection the newly embodied individual is dependent. These two primal beings provide the spit and straw with which the first persona is formed. It is the foetal personality. Just as Your parental genes determine Your foetal body, so does Your parental culture determine Your foetal personality.

As everyone knows, all foetal personalities are deficient. By definition, they are not the best way for an individual to mobilize himself in the world. That creates a problem, because there is no way to mobilize action in the world without a persona or an estimate of Your capabilities and limitations: namely, who You are.

This is what is crucial: the foetal personality is always false. No matter how good or bad, how stable or instable, Your initial persona is false. The falsity lies in the fact that it is not You; it is the familial crust that has formed around You. This is a necessary but provisional state, just as the body's original foetal nurture is a necessary but provisional state.

Expressed simply, Your first persona is no more permanent than is the cocoon of a pupa. It is a transitional state.

I must say these things, because You have the misfortune of being educated, which means You have had drilled into You the nonsense that Your character is set, once and for all, during childhood – as if an invisible cookie cutter had cut out and permanently shaped Your personality.

It is not merely Freud who is to be blamed for this; all of traditional psychology takes the foetal persona as the fundamental persona. They have the naïve belief that the future is but a résumé of the past – that past parental influences combine to form the soul in the same way that parental genes combine to form the body.

But bear in mind that the body does not begin its actual life until it is hatched from the egg and begins its growth in the world. By the same token, the persona does not begin its actual life until it is hatched from the family egg and inaugurates its own growth.

That first persona is similar to having to wear hand-me-down clothing. It does not fit You. It is too tight, too restricted. The foetal personality is a limited personality.

You say You want to know me but do not know what is expected of You. In reply, I say that You must hatch Yourself. This means recognizing that almost everything You have heretofore believed about Yourself and Your world is false and provisional. This means that it is only now, right now, that Your persona is being created; and as You recognize this, Your old, too tight, hand-me-down persona is sloughed off like an old skin.

To recognize that You lack fixity and that You lack a defined self is the only way to open Yourself to the living reality of always being a question that has no answer. If You can't do that, Your soul will never escape from its cocoon. It will rot.

You must come out of Your shell. You did not possess Your own body until You came out of the foetal shell, and You will not possess Your own soul until it emerges from the family shell. At the moment it hatched, Your body became "there." At the moment Your soul hatches, You will be "here."

I know You have come a long way from Your initial persona, but You have not yet shaken free of the original roots of dependency. To become free, You must see all of Your past as a mere preface to this present moment.

Now You know what I expect from You. I expect You to be a human being—not a humanoid. I expect You to be a butterfly—not a chrysalis. I expect You to fly up out of Your past, recognizing only futurity. At that moment You will have full claim over Your life and its flow. You will be just as I am: as much "here" as You are "there." Then we shall be able to communicate.

As I mentioned earlier, getting to know me is no simple matter. In order to know more about me, You must become more like me. You must stand up and look at me with a level gaze, daring to think of Yourself as my equal.

Are You able to dare such freedom? Are You audacious enough to look at me with a level gaze? Would it not be easier just to curl up in a foetal position and make Yourself small and humble?

Why not follow the tradition of all Your fellows and confess that You are weak and unworthy? In that way You can lie on Your back, awed by me, mistakenly believing my power to be "there" rather than "here."

Who on Earth do You and Your fellow humans think I am? Your father? Your mother? What a miserable presumption! How very religious!

I have already told You that I am not who You think I am. Now I wish to make another thing indelibly clear: You are not who You think You are.

Yours,
Fred

A Lonely
Little Girl

It was late Sunday morning when Fred finished his letter. Toward the end, as he was saying, "How very religious!" there was a curious coincidence: church bells sounded in the distance. Later on, about noon, I heard them a second time.

In the wake of Fred's letter, I had once again fallen into a fit of soul-searching. I suppose it was unavoidable, given some of the things he had written. It appeared that I was not too unworthy to be able to communicate with him. Fine. That wasn't a problem. But now another issue was raised: was I too incompetent to do so? Or, worse yet, too afraid?

That was only one of the things bothering me. During the afternoon, my thoughts kept coming back to the coincidence of the church bells and the "How very religious!" remark. It made no sense. It seemed indisputable that Fred was, in some fundamental sense, "religious"; otherwise, how could he be the center of worship of so many religions, whatever name they called him?

I had a fairly good idea of what Fred thought about theology: that it missed the mark. However, the ideological musings of theologians were a different matter from the devotions of millions of humans universally who personally worshipped Fred.

By the middle of the afternoon, my curiosity had peaked. I was certain he had made that remark intentionally to arouse just this kind of reaction in me. The more I thought about it, the more I was convinced that he had planted that "How very religious!" remark just to see how I would respond.

I decided to respond. It was Sunday; surely, more church bells would be ringing before the day was over. It seemed appropriate to go back into the study once more, sit down in front of the yellow pad, and write the following:

Dear Fred:
  Would you tell me about religions?
                         Yours,
                         Tom

The reply was not immediate. I waited at the desk for about ten minutes, but nothing happened. Then I went out on the patio and sat for awhile, watching the small birds dart about in the acacia trees.

It was a half hour before I began to feel the now familiar tugging on my right shoulder blade. A soft feeling moved upward, spilling over the top of the shoulder and coursing slowly down my arm like a warm liquid. I was already up and moving toward the patio. The feeling had reached my hand by the time I sat down at the desk. I smoothly picked up the pen, the fingers dropped down to the paper, touched, and began to write:

Dear Tom:
  Well, You seem persistent about wanting to know me. All right, then, I will fill You in on some of the curious facts about religions. But at the very outset, keep this mind: inasmuch as I am not who You think I am, it follows, quite logically, that religions may not be what You think they are.
  With that prefacing thought before us, let me suggest to You that the curious thing about religions is their prankishness. They are institutions that love playing pranks on everyone. The holy

prank is to claim that they, the religionists, are the only avenues for finding me, whereas in point of fact, they are just the opposite: they are absolute dead ends. Religions are not in the least concerned with access to me; rather, their holy role is to provide substitutes to replace me.

Religions did not originate with that purpose in mind. It just worked out that way. The result is one of the fine ironies of human history: those institutions claiming to be the most devoted to me are the most rigorously committed to steering humans away from me. That is the holy profession.

Religions are founded on feelings – deep feelings. Don't You remember that? Can't You still feel those profound surges that first rumbled in the depths of Your being? You were in Your teens when You began to experience those inexpressible feelings.

They were intensely meaningful feelings, weren't they? There was nothing illusory about them. They were disturbingly real for You, the child of Waco, Texas, trailing behind You fourteen years of innocence – and, all of a sudden, this strange upheaval began taking place in Your core.

Do You remember how grand those feelings were? They were so ponderous that no words, no concepts were large enough to embrace them. It was as if some overwhelming force had risen up out of Your roots and was taking possession of You.

But You did not mind those disturbing feelings. Do You recall? You savored those wondrous stirrings of Your roots. Voiceless questions seemed to be arising – questions so enormous that they were forever beyond answering.

Yes, I know what You are thinking. They were sexual feelings, undoubtedly; but the sexuality was so inchoate, so primal, that all time and existence seemed implicated.

To the degree that the feelings were sexual, it meant many, many things. It meant love. But it also meant joy. It also had to do with birth and with the overcoming of death. Still again, it meant bonding – communion with another. It meant the risk of guilt and the fear of judgment. It meant the scary prospects of adulthood and all that this state is heir to.

Thomas, those religious feelings were the stirring of Your second persona. Your manhood was rising up to meet You by embracing You with questions that hovered just beyond the reach of any answer. It was as if something at Your core were seeking to instruct You in the basics of life, and doing so by drawing from the deck the most elemental cards — the perennial cards You would be playing with the rest of Your life.

One of those cards had to do with Your sense of self. Were You, Tom Hanna, truly as free and unfettered as You fancied Yourself to be? Was it not just the reverse — that You were the thoroughly conditioned product of Waco, Texas, with all its provincialism etched into Your heart and all Your thoughts and feelings predictable and obvious? Wasn't that feeling of freedom a pitiful illusion, ready to pop like a bubble when touched by the needle of reality — a reality that proclaimed that every word You spoke was first spoken by others, everything You learned was taught You by others, and every concept and aspiration was born from the soil and culture of a central Texas town?

Were You, unconsciously, controlled by early programming while believing, consciously, that You were free? Were You a helpless victim of Your cultural programming, or were You a self-determining individual?

What was the answer? There wasn't any, and that is just the point. The question was like a dissonant chord which resists resolution into harmony, so much so that the dissonance appears to be patterned into the fabric of human existence.

Now hold onto Your hat. I am going to tell You a secret. It was I, Fred, who was playing the disturbing music which flooded Your young soul. The dissonance was an antiphony of the trumpeting sounds of freedom mixed achingly with the diapason of slavery. Just the sort of thing Mahler liked.

But — and here's the point — You listened to this unresolved antiphony, and its dissonance brought You awake. Your self-awareness was heightened to the point of ebullition.

Are You actually free? Or are You actually a slave? These are not ordinary questions; they are extraordinary questions. More importantly, they are Your questions for You to contend with perennially.

You can see how it works: questions without answers are higher-order questions — they project You into the perennial flow of life itself, whereupon You realize what answerless questions really are. They are possibilities.

Are You free? It is possible. Are You a slave? It is also possible. Both are always possible — not just now, but tomorrow and all the days after tomorrow. Never during Your life will there be a time when either option might not become possible. The unresolved dissonance will reverberate in Your being until Your last breath. You will never be quit of it because at any given moment the opposite is always possible.

That was what started happening when You were fourteen. Your troubled heart was instructing itself in the basics of life. On the surface, these basics seem paradoxical. They are not. A paradox is a question that does not yield an answer; but, if You are not looking for an answer, there is no paradox. Instead, there is only a possible way of living.

Which brings up another question that stirred within Your Texas cocoon: death. You sat with Your relatives in the room where Your grandfather was dying. You were nine. All of You waited and watched. His eyes were closed. He had been in a coma for three days. Then, on the afternoon of the fourth day, everyone was startled: suddenly, he began to move; his eyes opened and his throat made gutteral sounds as if he were going to speak. Because You had never heard a death rattle or seen the quiet, still gaze of the dead, You thought he was waking up. Even directly observed, death veils itself with life.

That was only the first time. There was the second time when Your older brother died — just like that, without preparation or warning. A simple, abrupt accident and Jack was no more. You were fourteen, and You knew that never again would You hear that voice or see those wonderful eyes. One day Jack was alive; another day he was not. You were robbed of his presence from then on, and there was nothing at all You could do about it. On that day, You discovered sheer helplessness: You could never change what death had done.

This raises a question: why should there be life if it ends in no life? Is life merely an illusion that ends with the reality of death? Or is death the illusion obscuring the enduring reality of life? But there was not any answer for You — only the question, its dissonance echoing down the corridors of all Your days to come.

I will tell You another secret: it was my *question and* my *dissonance You were hearing. That was not the end of it: as innocent as You were at that time, You still kept bumping into guilt. In fact, one always feels innocent until something occurs that provokes the opposite feeling of guilt. Even now, in Your middle age, You still feel more or less innocent, as if that were the official state of Your being. But if You will permit Yourself to recall certain things You have done and said and thought during the last ten years, looking at these things in a certain moral light, You will realize You are as culpable as the worst scoundrel. So, are You a man of innocence, of guilt, of both, or neither? The answer is not at all satisfactory: all four options are possible, and all are subject to change.*

It is the same in Your dealings with others. You are ready to judge others at the drop of a hat. Even with a friend it happens: one deviation — especially if it upsets Your composure — and You are suddenly as judgmental as the mythical Jahweh. Once You have isolated Yourself out on that limb, the only way back is to forgive, which is hellishly difficult because it, too, disturbs Your composure.

Back then at fourteen, just as now, Your heart was always vacillating between judging or forgiving Your fellows, just as You vacillated between feeling guilty or innocent in regard to them. What a crunch that was! But it was all right, because Your heart was instructing You in higher truths: namely, the never-resolved possibilities of life.

Then — as if You did not already have enough to contend with — there was love. At that age, Your feelings of love were unabashedly Wagnerian, with the horn section playing at full volume. Oh, those overwhelming dreams of merging with another human being! To become as one — her identity and Yours becoming the same. However, the dreams rubbed against the sober reality that unity with another was not possible; at best, one could be linked with another human through something shared in common — being of the same religion, the same ethnic group, or the same obsession. In that way, Your life could overlap with another's in the experience of community. Was the dream of unity only that — a dream?

It is no minor question: can You ever know another person directly through union, or must You settle for second-best: indirectly through communion? What is the final answer? There is none. Either remains equally possible. An unresolved dissonance quivers continually like a Bartok string quartet.

Now take all of these profound religious feelings and add them up. The result is a soul that is both disturbed and aroused. Are You, finally, a slave, or are You free? Does Your life end in death, or is there continuity? Can You always be forgiving of others and Yourself, or must You forever end up judging others while they, in turn, judge You? Can You merge with another human in total unity, or can You do no more than share a common identity?

These are the extraordinary questions You entertained during the florescence of Your youth. They are all unresolvable. That is what makes them higher truths: they constitute a firm and lasting foundation for the building of a human life.

I am saying no more than what You already knew at fourteen: the only way to build a stable life is on an unstable foundation. Inasmuch as the deepest truths about life are its uncertainties, You must keep these uncertainties resolutely in mind if You wish to live in the truth. To escape the uncertainty would be to escape the truth: in which case, to live in certainty would be to live a lie.

Yes, I know: You are not too sure about this. You are thinking, "That makes no sense. How can anyone live a stable life on an unstable platform?" A good question. But let me ask You a better question in return: "How can human beings keep their balance while standing on only two legs?" Think about that. I hope You get the point. It would not be possible for two legs to be more stable than four or six or eight unless the creature was genetically programmed to function better on two legs.

Look at Your body, and it will tell You something about Your soul: the human body – like the human soul – can function well only in instability. Only then is the whole system aroused and all the equipment used. The soul can be fully used and developed only on the unstable foundation of life's uncertain verities. Without the nourishment of uncertainty, the soul remains like a foetus riveted to the womb. The egg never hatches.

Br'er Rabbit belonged in the briar patch because that was where he was born and bred. Uncertainty and instability are the briar patch where You were born, and that is where You belong. This is not only where Your truth is; it is also where Your glory is. To turn away from it is to lose Your birthright. To give up the essential conditions for Your soul to grow would be tantamount to giving up Your soul.

Bearing all this in mind, I want You to remember something else that happened during Your fourteenth year. When all these troubling uncertainties began to rise up in Your soul, who was it in Waco, Texas, that understood Your turmoil? Who reached out to You? Who cared about the malaise You felt? Why, of course! Religious people cared. More than anyone else, they recognized and sympathized with Your perplexities.

Try to remember something else: what did they do with Your uncertainties?

Yes, now You are beginning to understand me. By the same token, You are beginning to understand religions, the function of which is to destroy uncertainties and replace them with certainties – to replace instability with stability. In brief, it is the function of religion to take away Your soul and, thus, to take You away from me.

Religions are roguishly clever. Faced with a fourteen-year-old boy who was just waking up and hatching his soul, what did the religious folk of Waco do? You remember quite well: they "saved" Your soul by persuading You that they had the answers to life's unanswerable questions. And from what did they "save" Your soul? They "saved" it from the uncertainties and unstable truths of life. They "saved" You from me.

Another thing: do You remember how it felt, at fourteen years of age, to be "converted"? As You lurched down the aisle, tears in Your eyes, to "accept Jesus Christ as Your Lord and Savior," You could hear the hymn they were singing: "Earnestly, tenderly, Jesus is calling, calling, 'O sinner, come home.'"

"Come home"– that is the eternal theme of religions. Can You remember the feeling You had when You "came home"? Yes, it was precisely that: the feeling of coming home.

Think about that. Here is a fourteen-year-old, stirring with the truth of life and just about ready to peck his way completely out of his parental shell, who all of a sudden becomes so

*sinfully ashamed of his stirring and pecking that he "repents"
and "comes home," leaving him right back where he started.*

*The expression for this is, I believe, being "nipped in the
bud." What a dodo You were. You surely recall that the dodo
was a bird, now extinct, that could not fly because its wings
never developed. The dodo is an ideal symbol for religions. If
there were truth in advertising, the image of the dodo bird
would be graven above the portals of every church, synagogue,
mosque, and temple.*

*Even though I am trying my best not to sound too serious, I
do not want You to take me as frivolous. To explain the nature
of religions forces me to walk a fine line between two attitudes:
one is that religions are the great tragedy of human history; the
other is that religions are the great joke of human history. As
You may remember, Your President Lincoln said that, at certain
moments, he laughed so as not to cry. That is a fine line.*

*It is a sad moment, indeed, when religions persuade humans
to "come home." They succeed in doing so by manipulating one
of the most powerful forces in the human system: the original
dependency and loyalty that all humans feel for their parents.
That was what they did to You. At the very moment when You
were ready to flap Your wings and learn to soar on the unstable
winds of life, You were persuaded that this was a sinful error.
At the very moment that Your face began to turn toward auton-
omy and Your back began to turn away from parental dependency, You were diverted – not converted – by the dodo
argument that others more knowledgeable than You knew the
answers to those disturbing questions which You could not
honestly answer.*

*Consider what this meant: by doing this, You denied Your
own experience and, instead, gave in to someone else – someone
who knew the final answers, someone who cared for You, loved
You, and wished to protect You from harm. Does that sound
vaguely familiar? Does it not sound like the family? Listen*

carefully: behind the voice of priestly assurance and rabbinical certainty and pastoral guidance, You will hear the primal voice of authority upon which You originally depended. It is the voice of Your parents. Every ounce of religious authority comes from the trust and dependency that all humans originally have for their parents.

Religions do not attempt to hide this fact. To the contrary, they advertise it: "If You don't mind, please address our priests as 'Father.'" That is being up front about it. However, they do not stop at that. They round out the family authority by suggesting You call their monks "brothers" and their nuns "sisters." If You still haven't gotten the point, they will insist that You refer to the Priest-of-priests as il Papa! You, in return, will be referred to as "my child."

Isn't that a prank? Isn't it a joke? Or is it a tragedy? If You do not take this seriously, then it is a joke. However, if You do take it seriously, look out!

The Protestants, of course, will have none of this. They are of a different mind — and tactic. "There is no need to address our clergymen as 'Father'; just say 'Pastor.'" Do You see how clever they are? In that way, You are led by Your own form of address into admitting that You are a sheep ready to be led.

Religions, no matter what their particular form, all speak with the voices of Father and Mother, whispering, "Believe in us, depend on us, follow us, trust us, and stay with us forever"— which is another way of saying that religions reaffirm Your foetal personality and its dependent state. Indeed, they give ultimate sanction to the state of being dependent. They finalize it, just as they finalize the profound and unanswerable questions of human life by pretending they can answer them.

Do not forget, dear Thomas, that religions always answer questions with authority. In their myths and sacred writings and rituals and preachments they assure You that the unanswerable has been answered once and for all time. They tell

You, "This is the case, and thus You are to accept it as the final truth." But hold on a minute. Whose voice is speaking these words? It sounds very much like Your father and mother – either, or both. The priests and the rabbis are daddy and mommy, now enshrouded in black and possessing the same absolute certainty that daddy and mommy once had about what is good for You and what is bad. The authority invites the same past obedience.

By and large, religions represent the family-of-families; like families, they control behavior by insisting on obedience. That is why religious institutions typically prefer authoritarian governments: they share the same belief system. Just peek behind the beard of the rabbi or the ayatollah or the Buddhist master or the Hindu priest, and You will discover the face of the father. Because You have been habituated to that face and its authority, religions always seize You in their profound and primitive way. They are fanning embers that were first lit when You entered the world.

This is the kind of prankishness that leaves me hovering between amusement and despair. It is all so transparent. The primary duty of religions is to prevent human souls from hatching – to "save" them from such a fate. Thereby, they preserve the foetal persona of life's first phase, preventing the development of the autonomous, adult persona of life's second phase.

You wanted to be told about religions. Well, there You have it: the goal of religions is to take my place, substituting themselves for me. They stand like a wall, a "mighty fortress" between me and humankind, deflecting all human impulses toward personal growth and freedom.

They compound this offense by claiming to be my spokesman; in other words, they take my name in vain. Christians kill Jews in my name, and Jews kill Muslims in my name. Muslims kill Hindus in my name, and Hindus kill Sikhs in my name.

Catholics kill Protestants in my name, and Protestants kill Catholics in my name.

All this swinishness has absolutely nothing to do with me. Their holy grounds are places soaked in blood, and their temples are monuments to my absence. I neither dwell in their temples, nor watch their rituals, nor hear their prayers. As a matter of principle, I have no more to do with religions than they with me: namely, nothing.

These are some of the curious facts about religion that I promised to tell You. Religions are founded on their presumption of the death of God. But that is not the worst of it. The real tragedy is that they thrive on the death of the human spirit.

There is a traditional expression for religious people: "God fearing." This is ironically true: the religious person is someone who has been taught to fear me and to do everything possible to escape me. Such people are afraid of the tendencies of their own souls. They are afraid of selfhood. And so, backward they fly, cleaving to the Father and wallowing in the dependence promised by the Father.

Excuse me, Thomas, but I cannot bear to speak further about this. I find it painful. Religion is a great, aching thorn in my side. It hurts when I think of the enormous loss and waste it causes. It hurts, because I am not who they think I am.

I am not Your Father. I am not Your Almighty God. I am not Your Judge. I am not Your King. I am not Your Shepherd. I am not these things any more than You are, in turn, a child, a weakling, a disciple, a sinner, a follower, a servant, or a sheep.

If You want to know me, You must realize that I am none of these things — and neither are You. Do not think of me as a father. Do not think of me as a male. Do not even think of me as old.

If You want to know me, think of me as someone very different, someone much younger: as a girl — as a little girl who is happy that You really want to know me. You might think of me

*as a little girl who is just starting out in life, who is somewhat
lonely, and who wants ever so much to find a friend.*

Yours,

Fred

Her timing was just right. At the very moment that I finished
writing, another bell pealed in the distance.

The Kiss

Fred's long letter had an astonishing effect. Something long forgotten was reawakened in me: my sense of the "religious."

I vividly remembered all the adolescent feelings he had mentioned. It was a happy surprise that those feelings had never ceased to exist within me; rather, they had been only momentarily repressed by the youthful atheism that had emerged in the course of my first philosophical fulminations.

At that time, I had forthrightly rejected religion; unthinkingly, I had thereby rejected the powerful stirrings that had led me toward the trap of religion. The baby had been thrown out with the bath water, and I had turned away from a part of myself which, nonetheless, had quietly continued to ferment.

To a large extent, Fred had succeeded in explaining me to myself. Why did I, an atheist by my nineteenth year, choose nonetheless to attend the University of Chicago Divinity School? I had not attempted to hide my atheism from the officials at the school. I told them my interest was in moral philosophy and—philosophy departments at that time being desiccated by scientific thinking —believed that a sophisticated theological curriculum was the best possible place to pursue that interest.

I now could understand why I had been so unaccountably happy at the Divinity School: without clearly understanding it, I was keeping alive those same questionings—the ones that Fred called the "stirrings of my roots." Apparently, the more I said "No!"

to all the religious answers I had learned about, the more I was fanning those fourteen-year-old's embers and saying "Yes!" to them. I had to laugh at myself. I had gone through theology school in the style of a Spanish dancer, turning my back disdainfully on religion while looking back at it over my shoulder with a smoldering gaze.

During the ensuing week, my head flashed with sudden memories of my boyhood—odd sentiments, shadowy reminiscences, and fleeting visions. I even recalled a strange event in my childhood which, amazingly, had not been obliterated from my memory. It was the memory of something I had done when I was scarcely more than four or five years of age.

It was summer, and I was living on Parrot Avenue in Waco. I was alone that afternoon because all of my playmates were taking naps. It was the unspoken rule of the mothers in the neighborhood that their small children were to take a two-hour nap after lunch. This was more for the mothers' peace of mind than for the children's sake. My mother had wanted me to do the same, but she had finally given up, because I was always too restless to sleep and too noisy to keep in the house. So we came to an understanding: *she* would take a nap, if *I* would stay outside the house during that time.

I do not recall what it was I did with myself during those times. I was still too young to ride a bicycle, so I was more or less restricted to the neighborhood. What I remembered took place one July afternoon when I was scampering around the hot, sun-soaked streets. It was quiet. The streets were empty. No sounds came from the houses as I passed by. It was as if the world stood still in slumber, and I was alone in the midst of it.

I had been exploring, two blocks away on Lasker Avenue, and I remember coming back by 31st Street, which led down to Parrot Avenue. I was walking past Mr. Spencer's house, which stood on the corner half a block from my own house, when a big cloud slowly passed over, scattering drops of rain—just a brief sprinkle that scarcely lasted a minute, but it caught me by surprise. It was an unexpected respite from the midday heat.

I stopped near the corner and looked down at the sidewalk. As if by magic, big, soft dots of brown wetness began to appear on the hot surface of the concrete. I was mesmerized: one drop after another would appear on the sidewalk, round and dark, and then gently disappear as others fell to take their place.

As I watched this, I became aware of a wonderful odor rising up from the hot, moistened sidewalk. It was a musty, earthen odor with an indescribable cleanness and sweetness. In a trance, I looked down, watching the wet dots appear and disappear while I sniffed the moist, stony odor. After a few moments, without knowing why, I lay face down on the sidewalk, coming into direct contact with that compelling odor. Then I opened my arms and did a strange thing: I embraced the sidewalk and kissed it. After a bit, I got up and went on my way.

It was such a mysterious incident. There was a purity about it that defied understanding. After almost fifty years, the vision of those wet, brown spots and their musty odor returned to my awareness with an immediacy that was almost the experience itself.

There was an immense, secret significance in my action that I could not then appreciate. What I did—and why I did it—remains wrapped in mystery, yet the earthen purity and cleanness of the experience were vivid and clear.

Upon remembering this event once again, I could not help but ask, "Was that you, Fred? Was it you I embraced? Was it your sweetness and purity I smelled?"

All week I was flooded with reminiscences. Something within me had obviously opened up. Some primal, terribly important region was once again making itself felt—something so fundamental that it seemed that the foundation of my being had been laid open and was revealing itself. I sensed that I was realigning myself with the transparent depths from which my life had arisen.

Yes, Fred was giving me back myself. How unexpected all of this was! I had told Fred that I wished to know him. And what had happened? He was causing me to know and remember myself. Was this what he meant about being "here"? Was this what was now happening—that I was becoming more "here"?

Perhaps—but maybe being "here" involved more than recollecting myself. By re-experiencing my own beginning, I was somehow remembering Fred who was "here" from the beginning. Perhaps he had always been "here," like a forgotten playmate of my earliest years of life.

But I said "he." That is incorrect. Who had it been, in that transcendent moment, that I kissed and embraced and smelled? Perhaps it was my first playmate and my first, secret love: a lonely little girl.

Alignment and Misalignment

During the five days from Sunday to Friday, I suspended the letter writing. I needed time to absorb the effects of that long letter.

On Monday, as I worked with my clients, every move I made seemed to be accompanied by strange reminiscences, and I would pause, suddenly visited with a luminous memory. All day long, I was seeing forgotten scenes, hearing long-ago sounds, feeling antique emotions—even smelling and tasting sensations which should have been totally beyond recall.

All my senses seemed awake and stirring with peculiar rumblings. It did not bother me, however. To the contrary, I was luxuriating in the richness of it.

I followed my usual work schedule. I saw four clients in the morning, went home at noon, skipped rope on the patio, and ate lunch. After lying in the sun for a half hour, I showered, dressed, and returned to the office to work with four more clients. The day finished, I returned home and poured a glass of chenin blanc, which I took out on the patio to sip while watching the crows gathering overhead for their raucous evening ritual of circling about the sky for a half hour before retiring to the rookery up the hill.

The evening came on, gradually peeling away the blue of the sky, leaving in its place a gray wash that slowly turned a gentle pink. This coloration lasted only a moment, the nostalgic pink soon settling down into an intense purple that continued darkening until finally stretched above me was a vast firmament stained with indigo. Then, one by one, the stars began to appear.

The night hours, just like the day's, were filled with recollections and rediscoveries. My past was uncovering itself, layer by layer, like shades of dusk falling into night. From out of the darkness, bright points of reminiscence appeared. And I, the passive spectator of this recollective process, was happily surprised to discover that the past, at least for the moment, seemed to contain more discoveries than the future.

This recollective process continued until Friday. By that time, it seemed to have worked itself out. I suppose I had absorbed all the effects of the last letter, for I was now feeling quiet inside—less dreamy and much more myself.

I decided that the reason Fred's letter had had such a strong effect on me was because the tone of address had become more personal. Fred had pointedly referred to special events in my life, as if my remembering and recognizing these experiences were somehow a way of knowing him—or her—better.

Apart from the refresher course on the religious wellsprings of my life, the tantalizing part of Fred's letter was the way it had ended: to think of him as not old, but young—and, indeed, as a little girl. At certain moments, when I thought of the sidewalk and the kiss, I could almost bring myself to feel that an invisible little girl had been there; but as soon as I thought of the Fred I knew from his earlier correspondence, I found myself feeling instead that I was being addressed by an older male.

Whether at the heart of reality there was an old man with a beard or a little girl with a skirt made an enormous difference. There had to be a difference in the manner in which we would think about the universe; yet, for the life of me, I could not imagine what it was. Every single religious tradition assumed that Fred was ancient—a long-lived being of total wisdom and rectitude. So what kind of universe was it, if there were a small, female child lurking behind the scenery of the cosmos rather than an old wise-beard? Surely this made a radical difference, but I could not figure out why.

These were the thoughts pressing in on me Friday evening as I opened the bottle of chenin blanc, poured a glass, and watched the spectacle of crows swirling about in circles. Presumably, such trivial questions as age and sex were too ordinary to apply to Fred. But it seemed to me now that ordinary questions such as these were unavoidable.

If he said, "Think of me as a little girl," then he meant this in relation to me; namely, I must think of Fred as younger than myself. That seemed strange. How could I think of Fred as a child in relation to me, an adult, without thinking of myself as somehow superior to him? That perplexed me.

Yet I know that it bothered Fred if I thought of him as superior and all-powerful and, thus, of myself as dependent and weak. But you cannot have it both ways. My relationship with Fred—my very desire to know him (or her)—seemed utterly dependent on the factors of age and sex. If either varied, so did the respective superiority or inferiority of the relationship.

I was feeling uneasy about the situation. It had revealed a terrible flaw in my character: I simply could not make myself feel that a little girl was superior to me.

But wait a minute: if Fred *were* a little girl, then it follows that Fred was, by definition, a little girl who was superior to me. Nonetheless, the logic of the situation had no bearing on what I felt; unfortunately, I felt respect for Fred only when I visualized him as an older man. As soon as I imagined him as a little girl, I felt a mixture of compassion and playfulness. Thus, there was no escaping the fact that a different age and gender created a different feeling and a different relationship.

Throughout dinner I continued mulling this over until it became obvious I was caught in an impasse. I did not delay seeking a way out. I got up from the table, went out the kitchen door, across the patio, and entered the study. I sat down, took out the yellow pad, and wrote the necessary question:

> *Dear Fred:*
>   *Are you, in some sense, younger than me and more female?*
> > > *Yours,*
> > > *Tom*

It was not a long wait. Within a few minutes, the warm feeling began in my shoulder and went straight to the hand. The pen dropped and spelled out the reply:

> *Dear Tom:*
>   *Yes.*
> > > *Yours,*
> > > *Fred*

There was the answer in black and white. Somehow, I would have to adjust to it. If I were going to know Fred, I would have to think of her as very young, yet very superior. It was not going to be easy, but that was the course charted for me, and it seemed too late to turn back. I could go farther only by plunging in deeper.

I went to bed, nurturing the image of a little girl. I could see her running up and down the sidewalk. I imagined her playing hopscotch, jumping from square to square, and counting her numbers in a quiet, little girl voice. I saw her skipping rope as her hair bounced loosely on her shoulders. I saw her doing these things, all the while being mysterious, powerful, and superior.

But when I thought of her in this way, it was as if the little girl was not what she seemed to be. Instead, she had a deceptive appearance. Under that high brow and cherubic countenance lurked another being: an ancient, sapient creature who only looked like a little girl—like an old crone with the power of dissimulation.

I lay in my bed, uncomfortable with these images and feelings, knowing that my attempt to realign myself with Fred was not working. I had asked, and she had answered, but it was not an answer that I could live with. It had the effect of separating me from Fred rather than bringing me closer.

Then, while in full flight, my thoughts abruptly stopped, plummeting into stillness. I suddenly became aware of what I was just thinking: "I had asked, and she had answered, . . ." I had forgotten something crucial: Fred never responded directly to direct questions. Direct questions always received deceptive answers, like "Are you there?" "No."

I sat bolt upright, considering the implications. Then I got out of bed, walked down the hall, through the kitchen, and out the door to the study. I turned on the lamps and sat down at my desk. The tablet with its previous answer was still lying there. I wrote:

Dear Fred:
    Are you, in some sense, older than me and more male?
                  Yours,
                  Tom

The answer came right back:

Dear Tom:
    Yes.

                  Yours,
                  Fred

That was more like it. I returned to bed and immediately fell asleep, satisfied with the knowledge that Fred was all things to all people.

The Great Shout

Saturday morning began with an intrusion. After breakfast, I was standing at the kitchen door, idly gazing outside at the trees, when something caught my attention. It was a quick movement of something small and floppy under the plum tree. Then it stopped. I waited. It started again, vigorously flopping back and forth.

I saw a pair of long ears. A young deer was sitting in the shadows of the plum tree, twitching his ears each time a fly would alight. I had never seen deer in the inner yard. The area was completely surrounded by a wire fence that served to keep the deer out so that they could not come in and systematically devour all the plants in my yard.

I was extremely cautious in opening the door. Even so, the deer was alerted, and he promptly stood up. It was a young buck with burgeoning horns. I thought I remembered him from last summer as the yearling who had always accompanied his newly born siblings when they came looking for fruit under the grove of old plum trees thirty yards from the house.

The young buck, his eyes fixed on me, backed away a few steps. When he moved, I saw two more deer standing there. They were young and freckled, and they inched backwards as I quietly closed the screen door.

I stood still, and they stood still. We went through a period of waiting and staring. I glanced around to see if there were other deer in the yard, but no, the rest of the family was absent.

I wanted to find out what part of my fence they had jumped over or wriggled under. I took a step forward. They took a step backward. I took another step forward, whereupon they trotted quickly around behind the juniper bushes.

Then I heard some rustling sounds. I, too, moved around behind the junipers just in time to see one, then two, then three white tails disappearing over a drooping section of the wire fence. They trotted off a dozen yards into the meadow, and then stopped to watch me as I tugged upward on the wire, stretching it out again to its original height. When I turned and started walking back to the house, the deer had already dropped their heads and were munching the dry, golden grass.

It was the weekend. I had promised myself an afternoon rendezvous with Fred. It seemed time to venture further in the relationship. This time, I knew exactly what I wanted to say in the letter. So I spent the morning catching up on some correspondence; with that then out of the way, I made a short lunch out of a sandwich and some iced tea.

Last night, while trying to go to sleep, I realized how much I was bothered by the question of Fred's age. What did it mean if Fred were "young," "old," both, or neither? And what did it matter? I had already learned that ordinary questions were useless in revealing who Fred was.

I wanted to understand with whom I was communicating, but the confusion over Fred's age and identity had me nonplused. Surely, I was communicating with a "person"—a person responding to the name of "Fred"—and a "person" is a being living in time. Therefore, Fred must be temporal.

All right, but how could I really be sure of this, inasmuch as Fred was not at all an "ordinary" person? It seemed possible that Fred was not at all "in time." At least, there was an old notion that Fred was eternal. As I reflected on it, I had to admit the possibility that one could be eternally in time. But what did that mean?

I was confused. Since ordinary questions were pointless, what question could I ask that would persuade Fred to tell me how he related to time? But . . . that was it! One would never bother to ask how ordinary persons related to time, since it was already obvious. With Fred, the situation was reversed: since I was dealing with an extraordinary person, the question about temporality was exactly the question that needed answering.

It was a warm and windless day, so I went into the study and brought the yellow pad out to the patio, placing it on the white metal table. I pulled up a chair and sat quietly for a moment, clarifying what I should write—certainly not a question, but a request for information. This is what I put down:

Dear Fred:
  Would you tell me about your relation to time?
                                      Yours,
                                      Tom

While I sat waiting, a little breeze swooped down onto the patio, stirring the bamboo chimes. Briefly, they thrashed about, then fell silent again. As I listened to the silence, the soft pressures of Fred began to move through my shoulder, cascading slowly downward to my hand. The pen pressed down, and Fred replied:

Dear Tom:
  It takes time to write down the words, "Would you tell me about your relation to time?" so You Yourself are in time; and, since the words of this reply are arranged in a sequence taking time to unfold, then it stands to reason that I, too, am in time.
  All right, but what is it, exactly that You and I are "in"? Is time an abstraction, as most people think? If that be the case, then it is doubtful that anyone could be "in" it. But if time is not an abstraction, then what is it? Is it a container in which we are

all contained? That is certainly possible. Then again, the reverse of this might be true: that we are the containers in which time is contained. In that case, time would be in us, rather than we being in time. Do You follow me?

Quite apart from these niceties of logic, one fact about time is fundamental: it always involves movement.

Time begins when movement begins, and time ceases when movement ceases. It takes time to write or read "Would you tell me about your relation to time?" because the hand has to move from word to word, just as does the eye in reading. In both cases, the writing hand and the reading eye are moving through space.

So, You see, that another fundamental feature of time is that it is inseparable from space, which is always moving. No matter how abstract "time" and "space" may be when separated from one another, they become quite concrete when their possibilities are actualized in movement.

This is so much the case that time and space have genuine existence only in the fact of movement. Since everything everywhere moves, then time and space are everywhere.

Or You could switch it around and look at it this way: time is what happens to space when it moves. If space does not move, there is no time – nor, for that matter, is there any space.

Now, if You will follow me carefully and not let me trip You up, I will show how this works. In order for space to be, it must be in some place; but in order for it to be in "this place" rather than in "that place," there obviously has to be more than one place – even if it be only the eyes moving from one place to another. To be able to notice that one place is different from another place, You have to notice two times in a row. When we note two spatial points in sequence, we are moving our attention through time. Thus, there can be no space without time, and no time without space. That leaves us with this conclusion: all time and space exist as movement.

Well, Professor Tom, how does that strike You? Is it philosophical enough to suit You? If You prefer, we could sprinkle in a few more therefore's and ergo's and Q.E.D.'s. No? It is enough? O.K. then, let's say that this suffices for an initial conclusion.

But it does not take us very far, does it? What will get us beyond these philosophical niceties is a close look not at time and space, but at movement. You want to know about my relation to time? Well, it is obvious: it all boils down to my relationship with movement.

That is funny, You know, because talking about myself and movement takes us right out of philosophy and into autobiography. I mean that I find nothing at all abstract about movement. It is not merely concrete; it is also quite personal. In fine, when the world moves, it is I moving.

Surprised You with that one, didn't I? But that's how it is: all of time and space are born in movement, and all movement is born in me. Nothing more autobiographical than that.

So that You can understand who I am, I am going to take the liberty of telling You a story about something that happened a long time ago:

Once upon a time, I lay within the cold emptiness of the void, sleeping a dreamless sleep. This was before movement and, therefore, before time. Because of this stillness and time-lessness, mine was a measureless sleep. It was also a measure-less waiting. I slumbered outside the boundaries of time and space, enfolded in completeness and promise.

Being complete unto myself, I lacked nothing. All the pieces of an immense jigsaw puzzle were neatly stacked in place. All my functions were tightly joined. All my energy was securely held. I was a self-contained being of infinite density.

At that time, there was no observer – no one to see or know. But if someone had been there in the cold emptiness, I would have appeared different from the way I now look to observers.

Back then, in my original self-contained state, my body would have been seen as tiny and round — as a gray and smoky roundness buttressed against the surrounding emptiness. I was an infinitely dense ball of something in an infinitely empty ocean of nothing.

Every inch of the future cosmos was brooding within my slumber's embrace. The future galaxies of gases, suns, and planets were all coiled within the constraints of my sleeping body. An observer would not have seen a bright, sunlike object, but a dark presence enfolded within a smooth integument reflecting all heat and light back to the interior.

I sometimes fancy that if there had been observers stationed out in that primal void, they would have thought they were gazing at a human brain lying suspended in the heart of nothingness — a dark, orbicular entity in which all thoughts and all actions were roundly unified.

The most obvious biographical fact a primeval observer would have noticed is that I am one. Back then, there was no cosmos, but there was something else: my oneness. The oneness was so obvious that an observer would know with certainty that all things were one, not only at the beginning but always — no matter how far my originally compacted being uncoiled outward into the empty coldness. I was one before movement began, and I have remained the same since movement started.

In that respect, I never changed at all. My oneness was an original fact before the advent of time and space, because I was totally self-contained. Well, I am still totally self-contained. No matter how immense and complex my moving parts have now become, my oneness has remained unchanged.

Tell me, Thomas, what do You think happened when that protracted slumber came to an end? If You had been that primeval observer, what would You have seen when my potentiality became actuality? When the coiled sinews became uncoiled? When the constrained energy became unleashed? What would have unfolded before Your eyes when impenetrable darkness became light and dead stillness became movement? What would You have seen when the egg cracked and space and time spilled outward into the emptiness?

It was my bright destiny to awaken when the moment was full.

At that moment, You would have seen the dark, orbicular shape commence to smolder, its smooth surface for the first time suffusing a glow. At that prodigious moment, the doors and windows of my being were opening. The brooding power was preparing to pour itself outward.

The egglike shape took on a soft, smoky hue, gradually building its intensity until the surface of my body began to radiate a dawnlike rosiness, the pink blush gathering itself eventually into an ardent red and then metamorphosing gently into a glowing orange. Like a storm gathering, the intensity of my luminescence now thickened its coloration until a fierce and strident yellow appeared, its pulsing revealing the deeper uncoilings of my being. This pulsation heightened in intensity until a searing green was released from my core, streaming through the portals of my integument – a bright, pungent green light suffusing not only my body, but the space around my body.

Gradually, it became impossible to distinguish between my orbicular shape and the emptiness around it, because the emptiness was no longer empty: it was filled with light. The light of my photons, like raindrops falling outward, drenched the empty coldness, transforming it into verdant space. The radiating waves of light obliterated the undifferentiated void and brought spatiality into being.

The rising escalade of rainbow hues had still another level of intensity in store: as the searing green flamed outward, it gradually disclosed an underlying cast of blue that began pouring forth from my center – an intense, vibrant, explosive blue *which seeped into the pores of the void, imprinting it with an azure dye. Flames of blueness reached outward from my body, flickering tongues licking space and setting it aglow.*

Had You been there as a witness, You then would have seen the next stage of my awakening when the outpourings of my energy intensified yet again, now transcending the scale of visible colors and moving higher into the higher frequencies of ultraviolet radiation. You would not have seen this change, so much as felt it. From this point onward, You would have felt an ever-increasing vibration.

In awakening, I took possession of my world, and I did so by reaching out simultaneously in all directions. The void was unused, so I seized it. It was without heat, so I inflamed it. It was empty, so I filled it.

As the rush of energy and heat mounted, so did the vibratory motion. All space had been stirred alive with vibration – an immense diapason began to swell and shudder its way through the nascent universe. Then, nearing its peak, the vibrations ascended to an extreme pitch that produced the sound of a colossal keening. The keening flowed outward into the now glowing and vibrating universe, which responded by matching the frequency of my own internal vibrations. At that point, when the tuning fork of space and time resonated exactly with my inner song, the Great Shout went up. It exploded from the center of my being and rocketed forth into the quivering flesh of the universe. As the shout roared forth, so did the coiled strands of my being. Potentiality had now become actuality, and the long-pent-up energy sprang outward.

The Great Shout was the birth of the cosmos: time and space came into being and the great unfolding commenced. Movement began. I do not want You to confuse the Great Shout with what astronomers call the Big Bang. As a descriptive term for my birth, I find it demeaning – not only because a "shout" is not a "bang," but also because "bang" suggests a disorderly explosion. I hasten to assure You that my birth was not in the least chaotic. To the contrary, it was wondrously orderly and smooth. And it was precisely executed.

With the Great Shout, the interlocked pieces of the jigsaw puzzle began to separate, exfoliating outward from my centrum into space. From that crucial moment onward, it has unfurled itself in such unbroken skeins that, were there a way of reversing this unfolding, every formerly interlocked piece would fold right back into the centrum from whence it originated.

Presiding over this unfolding were the regulating hands of my oneness: the four forces of my cohesiveness are a strong force, a weak force, an electromagnetic force, and a universal force – gravity. They draw things together into an orderly community: particles form a tight quadrille; atoms are held together with the same cohesion; all bodies are drawn toward one another by positive attraction, but are kept from imploding on each other by the polite spacing provided by negative repulsion.

Gravity and its other three forces are my active principles of unity. They guarantee that everything is related to everything else, no matter how far apart everything expands. Gravity is, simply, my oneness reflected in the expansive fabric of my cosmic body. Before the Great Shout, I was a single, self-contained being; now, billions of years after my birth, I am still just as single and self-contained as ever. This is my "quantum" nature, which seems mystifying to everyone but myself. Obviously, every place within me is me. There are no empty places: there is no void that is not filled with my oneness.

From the beginning, all the rules for unfolding the jigsaw puzzle were in place. So the Great Shout was not simply the outpouring of my energy, but an orderly display of the scheme for this outpouring. You might think of energy as my "body," but You should also think of the laws of oneness as my "soul."

Look all around You, and You will see my body: it is the earth, the planets, the sun; it is all the planets and solar systems within the Milky Way galaxy; it is all the other galaxies still expanding and plummeting away from my original centrum; and it is all the dark matter and black holes filling the space between and within those galaxies. The cosmos is my awakened body, unfolding according to my rules.

You have asked about my relationship to time. So I want to call Your attention to one of the most curious facts about my unfolding: it did not happen instantaneously. I want You to think about that. Why did the entire unfolding not take place in an instant, like an authentic Big Bang – a firecracker that explodes, and that is the end of it? Why didn't my bright destiny completely unfurl itself in the twinkling of an eyelash? Think about the curious fact that billions of years have passed since my awakening and still the unfolding is not complete. How could that be?

I think the most revealing thing about my character is the fact that I did not end the process all at one time. Patience is built into my nature. Certainly, my rules of unity – all the cohesive forms of gravity – slowed things down a bit, but that is not the genuine sign of my patience.

The supreme sign of my patience is the speed of my light: it is finite, rather than infinite. If my light could go everywhere, instantaneously, the history of the cosmos would have ended almost as soon as it began fifteen billion years ago, but light, the fastest thing in my universe, is only relatively fast. It will travel 186,000 miles per second, rain or shine, and that is as fast as it will go.

It becomes curiouser and curiouser when You begin to understand what this means. It means that when one part of my body flashes a message to another part, the other part will have moved on in space, and so the message somewhat misses the mark. In fact, because light transmission is not instantaneous, it always arrives too late. It's a problem – that delay – but I can adjust to it. It's part of the process.

Another curious thing: my body is always moving, somewhat like that of a little girl playing hopscotch and imperturbably jumping from square to square. Because space and time are created by movement, each jump redefines "where" things are in space and "when" in time. What this means is that no part of me is ever fixed in the same place at the same time. In short, I am never any place in particular.

Seems irresponsible of me, doesn't it? "Where's Fred?" "Oh, he's nowhere in particular." But wait, it gets worse, because time is no more linear than is space. Some of my constellations, for example, are so far away from You that, as You now look at them, what You see is not the constellation as it is "now," but as it was billions of years ago when the light began traveling from the constellation to the Earth.

So, You see, parts of my body in the present tense are simultaneously in the past; similarly, the fact of Your present observation of the constellation will take billions of years before the news of it reaches the constellation and becomes "now." The upshot of this is that I am simultaneously past, present, and future — depending on which part of me You take as a reference point.

Be careful about one thing: just because I am beyond ordinary time does not mean that I am "eternal." Theologians think that I am temporally eternal and spatially infinite. That is their relative viewpoint. From my point of view, I am neither eternal nor infinite. Quite the opposite: I am utterly wrapped up in time, slogging through the process step by step.

Theologians blithely assume that I am above and beyond time, as if I were on a permanent vacation. Unfortunately, it does not work that way, and I wish theologians were more sympathetic with what I constantly have to undergo. The truth is that my process of unfolding is long, hard work. The fixed speed of light and all the gravitational rules of cohesiveness are the traits of character of someone who has work to accomplish.

There is no escape from it. The Great Shout was not over and done with instantaneously, and that leaves me with a task that I must pursue moment to moment and inch by inch. You must not think I am confessing my imperfections. It is not that. It's something quite different: it is my commitment *to work out my destiny through time and space – not my failing.*

Theologians prefer me to be virginally untainted by time and space, serenely sailing above the tossing seas of the cosmos. However, if they could see me as I see myself, they would instantly recognize that to understand me, the world, and even themselves means that they would also have to understand that we are all involved in a process that has not yet completely unfolded.

You, Tom, are not a theologian – just the reverse. Even so, I feel uncomfortable about Your reaction to what I have been saying. I am concerned that You might want to reject me, because of my apparent imperfections. To learn that I must labor my way through time and space – does it put You off? Does it make me less admirable than the role You would like me to play?

It would be dreadful if You felt that way. It would mean that the process of working one's way through time and space was despicable for You, and that would be a terrible misunderstanding – not only of who I am, but of who You are. For better or for worse, the process that I must go through is also Your process.

You surely must see that You and I have something very basic in common: we are both destined to grow, and we do so by adapting with the process of time and space. When I say that I have a "body" and certain rules of "character," I mean that literally; when I tell You that my body "unfolds," it is another way of saying that I am expanding and becoming more complex. And I have been doing just that for over fifteen billion years.

Fifteen billion years old! That's a lot of candles on the cake, and, from that perspective, You might think of me as old beyond measure. However, the fact that I have not yet completed my unfolding means that my life is still ahead of me — that I am, indeed, young and still developing.

You have no way of knowing just how "young" I am, any more than You have a way of knowing just how "old." I am, simultaneously, immensely older than You think and immensely younger than You can imagine.

The surprising thing about my relation to time is that it is the same as Your relation to time: we both are alive; we both have what we think of as "bodies"; we both move our bodies through time and space; and we are both still developing.

I am not trying to foist myself upon You as a companion, but, even so, I find it highly amusing that, despite vast differences between us, we share a common fate: even though I am fifteen billion years old and You are a mere fifty, neither of us is finished yet. Life is up ahead.

We share another similarity: we are both embodied and moving and, like all other organisms, have been growing and evolving from the beginning until now. Organic life bears its own continuity and history which unite its first moment with its latest moment. That is not only fundamental in understanding Your life and all organic life, but it is also fundamental in understanding me.

I think it best if You try to think of me simultaneously as my original slumbering and my present awakened being. You should keep in mind those two images of my compacted being and my exfoliated being, because they are two phases of the same continuous history. I was unified, just like an organism, before the Great Shout, and I am just as unified now. I have simply grown a bit — just like You.

Here's an image: imagine that there was once a great seed in the center of the All. Then, one day this seed opened and began to grow outward—"outward" rather than "upward," because a seed in the middle of the All cannot grow "up," but only outward in all directions at once.

Can You imagine a tree that grows only outward? Well, of course: on Earth. Trees in Australia, Russia, South Africa, and Canada—or any place else on Earth—grow from the same center, yet all of them grow outward in different directions. Right? That is exactly how I have grown: outward in all directions simultaneously.

A seed in the middle of the All grows outward in all directions—in quite the same way as light floods outward in all directions from a single lamp—and, so, rather than having a trunk going in one direction: "up," I have a trunk that goes outward in all directions. It is a strange tree for an Earthling to visualize: roots in the center, and everything growing outward and branching and then rebranching, like a tangled vine.

It is the same continuous tree from the beginning of its roots to the outward branching of its limbs and twigs, and I am the same continuous being from the roots of my past to the branchings of my present. No one can see that tangled tree. At no point in space can one see the original "center" where I once slept, nor can You obtain a clear view of the branches. Yet, despite the relativistic vagaries of space and time, the tree is all about You, moving and growing as it always has been—and You are nesting in its waving branches.

In conclusion, You now know what my relation is to time: it is the same as Yours. I am alive, and I have a body and a history, just as You do. Both of us share the fate of still being alive and feeling incomplete—the movement continues, and the action goes on. You and I are grasped by the same reality: both of us still have something to do that we have not yet done.

Yours,

Fred

As soon as I put down the pen, I realized I was exhausted. I sat back in the patio chair and looked up at the trees. I noticed that my vision was blurred; the glare of the yellow page was still in front of my eyes. The glowing pad had once again clouded my vision, stirring the nightmarish image of a few weeks ago when the elusive yellow glow was flapping around, just beyond my reach, like a giant butterfly.

It was some moments before the blurring passed away. I continued staring at the trees, feeling a bit numb. The leaves of the trees fluttered about under the urgings of an afternoon breeze. The leaves projected from twigs, the twigs projected from limbs, the limbs projected from branches, the branches projected from the trunk, the trunk projected from the Earth, and the Earth—what did it project from? Now I knew the answer to that one: the Earth projected from Fred.

Everything jibed. Everything that moved was connected. The pieces of the cosmic jigsaw puzzle were still neatly in place, nicely regulated.

Watching the leaves dance in the breeze, I had the overwhelming feeling of being in a different place. My "where" was different. Certainly, I was sitting on the patio, and the patio was in my little valley, but the valley, the patio, and I were all in a different point in space. Their relative position had mysteriously shifted, assuming a new place within an altered spatial situation. Nothing had changed, yet everything had become different. The world had become vastly expanded while, paradoxically, bringing me much closer to Fred. It appeared that space was far more relative than physicists had ever dreamed.

Time, as well, had been altered—certainly my own sense of temporality. An hour earlier, I had thought of myself as a man in his fifties who, on the scales of mortality, had more past behind him than future in front of him. I did not feel that way now. My past seemed small and insignificant—no more than a preparation for what was to come. Everything lay ahead, waiting to be done. My life was no longer a fact trailing behind me, but a possibility lying before me.

Because of Fred's letter, the relative parameters of time and space had undergone a change. I thought I understood how such a change could come about: since time and space are the movements of Fred, by changing my relation with Fred I had changed my relation to time and space.

As the leaves rustled high within the trees, I savored my amazement at what had happened: my desire to know how Fred stood in relation to time had ended in my discovering how *I* stood in relation to time and to space and to Fred—and to everything else.

A Drive to the Abyss

I began Sunday still savoring Saturday's letter. Late in the morning, I decided to take a drive. I got in the VW van and headed westward out of town, following the rolling valley that leads toward the sea. Dark green clumps of oak and bay trees nestle within the folds of the flesh-colored hills. Here and there, cows amble about, munching the crisp stalks of wild oats.

The creek bed running the length of the valley was dry. Further on, the creek ended abruptly against the great cement wall of the dam holding the waters of a lake, the source of our drinking water. Situated within a great bowl of mountains, the lake is a favorite nesting place for ducks and geese. In the distance, I could see hundreds of their tiny bodies bouncing in the water.

The road continues westward, now rising up into the mountains, then cresting the ridge to begin a slow descent toward the Petaluma-Point Reyes road, whereupon the lake road suddenly runs into a T. At that point, I turned left and drove past the country fire station and, further on, skirted the grounds of the Rouge et Noir cheese factory, where the county's copious supplies of milk are regularly made into round little Camembert and Brie cheeses.

Another dry creek bed appeared off to the left and trailed alongside the road as it gradually descended the trough of a long valley, ending in the broad-spread waters of the Nicasio Reservoir.

Soon, I turned right and crossed over a small, concrete bridge where the road leads to the little town of Point Reyes Station. Point Reyes is picturesque: it looks like a movie set for a wild West film. There is something else special about the town: it sits on the threshold of the Point Reyes Peninsula where the earth abruptly becomes a bed of granite. The Peninsula expands westward, forming itself into a great headland that thrusts its face into the sea.

The Point Reyes Peninsula is a geological oddity. Its granite eminence does not belong to the American continental shelf: rather, it squats on a geological plate that is part of the Pacific Ocean bed. This plate is ineluctably being dragged northward and westward into the cold waters of the North Pacific, steadily separating itself from the mainland.

The clear evidence of that separation is provided by the long, thin finger of Tomales Bay that begins just beyond Point Reyes Station and extends many miles northwestward straight as an arrow. The uncanny straightness of the long, inland bay is a tip-off of something slightly ominous: the bay's waters lie directly over the deep, straight crevasse of the San Andreas Fault.

When I reached Point Reyes Station, I crossed from one geological zone to another as I went over the fault line. I now drove along the west bank of Tomales Bay. Mile after mile, the waters stretch northwestward, marking the frontier of a continent. Beneath those waters to the right lurks an abyss where the Earth had been sundered in twain.

I could not help musing about the split that lay beneath me. What if the abyss suddenly opened, splitting the peninsula forever from its tenuous attachment to the mainland? I could almost feel the immense forces which, at that very moment, were grinding away under the face of the waters, the tectonic plates in relentless collision. Beneath those plates the crust of the still molten Earth floats upon the fiery, glowing magma.

As I came nearer the mouth of the Bay, where it widens to meet the ocean, the road swept away to the left, leaving the bay and rising over the granite hills before dropping slowly toward the Pacific on the other side of the peninsula.

The ride along the bay had been quiet with the calm of a summer's day, but now, as I approached the Pacific, the scene was dramatically transformed: huge, moaning onslaughts of wind dropped from the ocean skies and scoured the tossing grasses. In the distance, great roars from the pounding surf reached my ears, and I could see the sea throwing itself massively against the flanks of the peninisula.

I parked the car. As I got out, the whiplike wind folded itself around me, buffeting my eyes and ears with its frenzy. The humming sound was relentless and deafening.

I walked across the sand toward the ocean. It was anything but pacific. It was sublimely frightening: the wind and tide combined to produce waves of such dimensions and power that, approaching, they looked ready to roar up the beach and engulf the entire peninsula. Over and over, the howling waves threw themselves maniacally against the sand, grasping it, losing hold, beginning to slip back, and then desperately mounting a charge once again.

I stood as near to the ocean as I dared, not observing so much as experiencing this prodigious display of power. To enhance the experience, I closed my eyes. A surprising thing happened: I immediately saw the image of a dark, smoky roundness. But it did not remain dark. It slowly unveiled a rainbow of colors—red, orange, yellow, green, blue, indigo, violet. Above the roaring surf I could hear Fred's voice telling me that had I been present at the beginning, there in the void, I would have finally ended not by seeing, but by hearing and feeling the event.

I stood there, wind and sound pummeling my senses, but now I became aware of a distant, elusive sound that was mixed up with the noise that whirled about me. It was a tiny, intense sound seeming to emanate from the depths of the roar. I knew it was there, but it was difficult to distinguish.

I waited and, bit by bit, the tiny sound seemed to grow clearer and more distinct, becoming high and pure like an immense voice singing in the distance. Within a moment, I tuned in on the sound, hearing it steadily; as soon as I did so, my inner vision began to glow with a strange whiteness. The sound intensified and engulfed my very being. Now I knew what it was: the sound of keening. The intense sound and the pulsating whiteness took increasing possession of me, the molecules of my body seeming to resonate with it.

I was engulfed in a singing whiteness, and every particle of my being was vibrating with the keening song, a song that intensified and swelled in slowly accelerating waves, driving me relentlessly forward until the keening attained an almost unbearable intensity. At that instant, it happened: I heard a colossal voice roar forth, and the Great Shout rocketed through my being. Everything became incandescently white, and I was seized by the keening light, feeling the ground disappear from beneath me as I was sucked downward into a spiraling maelstrom. I began to fall. The abyss—the abyss had opened wide and was swallowing me into its maw. I was helplessly falling, with my senses reeling and the Great Shout impacting against the walls of my consciousness.

I was certain that I had died. It was all over. Then it happened again. Once more I was seized by that powerful force—a wrenching, lurching movement of the foundation dropping from beneath me. This time it was different: it was not my feet that felt the movement, but my cheek.

I was lying on the sand. Once again the sand wrenched and lurched, almost as if it were alive. I opened my eyes and looked about. Then I placed my hands, palms down, on the sand. Again, it shook, but not as much as before.

I should not have been surprised. It was a brief earthquake. The abyss had stirred. Nothing more natural, given where I was. But it had seemed unnatural—almost miraculous for a moment. I waited, my palms still pressed against the sand. No further tremors came: the earthquake was over.

There was a great deal of sand inside my shirt. I stood up and tried to shake the sand out of my clothes. The wind and the waves continued their roaring, but were now much less frightening and intense. I almost felt at home.

For an hour, I strolled along the beach, with an exhilarated feeling of liberation. I had no idea why I felt that way. And as I walked, I kept expecting the ground to shake again. I really wanted to feel once more the uncanny sensation of an unstable Earth—an Earth that was *supposed* to be there supporting me. The quake had reminded me of the support I had always assumed to be there beneath me. It was like a message from Fred, putting me on notice that he was my undergirding presence.

I had the peculiar notion that if the undergirding support were taken away, I—and all the creatures of the Earth—would plummet downward in space and backward in time, falling all the way back to that original, dark roundness from which all things had sprung.

Later, I drove back eastward over the crest of the peninsula and down to its lee side where Tomales Bay still remained wrapped in summer calmness. In the village of Inverness, I stopped and had lunch at Vlasta's, the little Czech restaurant that specialized in dumplings and red cabbage. Then I drove leisurely back through Point Reyes Station and onward to the Nicasio Reservoir, then the cheese factory, up the lake road, and finally back home.

But, once home, I had no desire to go into the house. Instead, I spent some time strolling along the creek and under the trees. I checked on the progress of the plum orchard. I was relishing the feel of the earth beneath my feet. Eventually, the afternoon grew late and quiet. The hush of the fading day crept into the grass and trees and hills, bringing with it a gentle sweetness.

I sat down near the plum orchard, watching the sky as it slowly darkened. Cool shadows began to well up in the hollows of my small valley. Looking upward, I saw the evening star appear in the western sky. Within a few moments, other stars appeared, until the heavens were overspread with millions of luminous dots as inscrutable as they were familiar.

I lay down on the grass and let my vision feast on the panorama unfurled above my gaze. I looked at no particular stars, but instead tried to drink in the sky with a single, undifferentiated gulp of the eye. In the distance, dogs were barking. I heard the voices of neighboring children up the hill.

The ground was beneath me, supportive and stable. The sky was above me, immense and deep. As I felt the earth and viewed the heavens, I heard a still, quiet voice say, "This is my body which is given for You."

I could not be sure whose voice it was—mine or Fred's.

The Ogre

During the next day and those which followed, I went about my business acutely aware of a subtle change in the way my body moved. I noticed that there was a difference in my walking: it seemed easier. At the point of contact between my foot and the ground, there was a soft, electric feeling. Formerly, I had simply felt my foot *against* the ground; now the ground had lost its feeling of solid opposition to my foot and, instead, seemed to lift upward into the foot. It was not a feeling of floating, but something much subtler: a feeling of being actively supported.

For the first time in my life, I began to feel the energy of gravity. It was as if something living were radiating upward from the Earth. Beneath my feet, I experienced an Earth that was so densely packed by its own gravitational pull that I could feel the planet as a single entity upon whose support I depended. I felt secure as I stood upon the Earth's outer shell. Somehow, it felt beneficent.

Because of this new sensitivity to what was beneath me, my walking had mysteriously turned into an action of gliding across the surface of the Earth. I moved through the air like a swimmer moves through water. I was feeling a soft, rotational movement in my pelvis, each side pushing forward as its leg reached forward. In addition to this horizontal movement, there was an up-and-down oscillation of the hips. Each time I brought my leg forward and placed my weight on it, I could feel the hip rise up, accepting that weight.

I was fascinated by the circularity of the movement created by the alternating horizontal-vertical displacement. The left hip lifted and circled, then the right hip lifted and circled, and both sides moved like two perfectly phased cogwheels.

It was uncanny: my walking had become easier. Instead of feeling effort, I felt only flowing pleasure, as if something inside me had taken over the mechanism of walking. It was not so much that I was walking, as it was that I was being walked.

I was experiencing something profoundly human—something genetically given to me that I had known as a child, but had later forgotten. It was a funny kind of knowledge—a knowledge of how to do something. This profoundly human knowledge was not of a *What,* but of a *How.* I experienced the effortless pleasure of gliding over the surface of the Earth, with my head and all its senses quietly pointing ahead and floating over a body whose pelvis and hips made smooth circles; as one leg went forward, the opposite arm swung forward, making the thorax and arms rotate one way and the pelvis and legs the opposite way.

What happened when I did this was that I felt more myself. I felt more human. I had allowed a genetic gift of *homo sapiens* to emerge and take charge of a basic life function; by doing this, my awareness had changed. Fred had made me more sensitive to the fullness of my inner being: I was not merely a passive observer, but an active doer. The most important truth about me as a human was not a fact, but a process—not a *What,* but a *How.* This How was so precise, so efficient, and so anciently in tune with the Earth: by learning to give in to it, I experienced a quiet ecstasy—the sense of moving in balance with the world. For some reason, the word *fair* came to mind. I was moving fairly, but I could not quite understand why this word seemed to fit.

The experience of walking forward into the world, smoothly and easily, is a prototype of the human experience of time: as my face moved forward into the air, I experienced the flow of the present moment moving into the future, pushed forward by my own initiative, creating my own future.

I was beginning to suspect that if we could strip off the illusions and misunderstandings we have of ourselves, we might discover ways of functioning far more efficiently and pleasurably—ways which, in a sense, would guarantee a higher level of mental and physical health than we have ever imagined.

It was not only the walking that was changed. I had, in general, the experience of being more in *connection* with the world—or, perhaps, of being in connection with *more* of the world. It was hard to say.

Yes, I was becoming more sensitive to what was beneath me. There was more beneath me—more complexity and more layers —than I had ever before sensed. I had heard that safecrackers develop such a fine ear they can hear the tiny movements of the tumblers within the lock. It is a skill that can be learned, and this was how it was with me: I seemed to be developing the skill of detecting subtle movements in the universe beneath me. What was below me seemed deeper, what was above seemed yet grander, and my connection with both seemed closer.

It was an exhilarating feeling, but it struck me as peculiar— surprisingly so, for it was not my soul that was being changed, nor my heart, nor my psyche. What Fred was changing was my *sensing* of where I was. It was a change in the way I processed my experience—that was what felt peculiar. By sensing more of myself, my self-control became more precise and efficient. Fred appeared to be using a radically untraditional approach to conversion. Or was it something other than conversion—an odd kind of education offering me not passive knowledge of a *What,* but active experience of a *How?*

I could appreciate the inevitability of what was happening. Everything had begun with my wanting to know Fred. As it turned out, however, I could do this only if I developed the inner skills and sensitivity which allowed me to appreciate him, and he was providing me with a ladder to scale if I wanted to reach his height.

The oddity was that the ladder ran downward rather than upward. It appeared that I had to descend, somehow, back through the tightly intertwined spiralings of Fred's evolved history to sense the oneness that was there before the beginning and that had continued unbroken right up to the present moment—here and now on this spot of earth.

Apparently, Fred was helping me to become more "here." He had said that he was already "here." To the degree that I learned to be *here*, I was coming to know Fred.

Well and good. But what was *my* connection with the oneness he was so emphatic about? I could understand that the physical universe was one—in its original compacted state as well as in its later unfolded state. Still, what did the oneness of the universe have to do with me, a living being?

I was not physical. I was organic—something quite different. What was the connection, if any, between my organic being and Fred's physical being? Gravity? That was a connection, surely, but it did not appear to account for much.

I let these thoughts simmer during the week. I felt a conflict: I was eager to receive another letter from Fred, yet I felt it important not to rush. Being enlightened by Fred had the effect of throwing into stark relief some obscure crevices that seemed dark and unconnected with what had been illuminated. Those shadowy crevices were, I suspected, the many pockmarks of my self-ignorance.

Just in case you are wondering about it, I should mention that I was not, during this time, going about like someone possessed. There was nothing in the least cockeyed about my behavior. Except for the new feelings I have mentioned, I believe I was more or less the same as always—in a way, just as skeptical. I was acutely aware of the craziness of what I was doing, but that was more than balanced by an even acuter awareness that I was, without any doubt, going through a transformation. Fine! I could use a little transforming.

Each time I sat down before the yellow pad, there seemed to be another Thomas looking over my shoulder and saying, "Tsk, tsk! There you go again, playing at being a psychic, pretending that the words flowing from the pen are not yours, but his." The other Thomas was right: I *was* playing the role of the automatic writer "channeling" someone else's spirit. For a skeptic, my situation had all the charm and horror of a Puritan lying drunk and debauched in a house of ill repute. I had the rock-hard conviction that automatic writing was a delusion. I really did not doubt that. But the embarrassing truth was that it was, nonetheless, happening: I was, unquestionably, discovering new things about myself, and I was being changed by the process.

It was the delicacy of this process which concerned me. My skepticism sat there like an ogre, watching over the shoulder of the poor lunatic who was corresponding with God. But the ogre could not speak; I would not let it. I felt, intuitively, that as long as I refused to allow my skepticism to verbalize itself, it would not interrupt this process.

In that sense, it was a game that had its own internal rules and had to be played out to the end, delicately, according to its own dynamics. For all I knew, this *was* how revelations happened—as a process that is accidentally triggered in the brain and, once it starts, is carefully guided through to its completion.

It was not the otherworldly nature of the experience that fascinated me. It was the information, which turned out to be very *this-*worldly. I was learning about myself, and this was reshaping my consciousness. The writing process had triggered something within me that dredged up large chunks of my past for reexamination. My recollection of the past was teaching me about the present.

All this new information was coming from the same place: me. Granted. But it came from me only because of the delicate game of pretension I was playing: assuming that I had become the instrument of Fred's word.

So, I waited—skeptical, hopeful, believing and unbelieving—all at the same time. I waited.

Inevitable
Since the
Beginning
of Time

I only waited until Friday. At four o'clock in the afternoon, I went into the study and sat down at my desk. I looked over at the bookshelf and contemplated the yellow pad sitting upright between the Ueberweg and the side of the bookshelf where I usually put it when I was done. I did not want anyone to see it lying open on my desk.

I kept my eyes fixed on the yellow pad while thinking of what I wanted to write in the letter. Once I had the phrasing right, I got up, removed the pad from the bookshelf, and placed it on the desk. Then I wrote these words:

Dear Fred:
You told me about your beginning, but you did not tell me about life's beginning.

> *Yours,*
> *Tom*

As I waited for the reply, something totally unexpected occurred. I experienced an abrupt pang of shock. Not only that: a powerful surge of anger seized me, sending a convulsive shiver down the front of my body. I knew instantly that I had made a mistake. Somehow, I had phrased the sentence badly.

Then I felt my arm roughly contract, and the pen was smashed heavily down against the paper. For a moment I thought it would rip through the yellow surface as the words poured forth:

Dear Tom:

Far be it from me to insist that Your billets-doux *not be dim-witted, shortsighted, and ill-considered. After all, it is a free cosmos, and everyone has the right to seek out the level of hebetude with which he is comfortable. But, damn it, given what You have just written me, it would probably be more appropriate if I sent You right back through the revolving door.*

We have already danced that minuet, haven't we? Perhaps, the responsibility is partially mine for going a bit too fast for You, and that is why You are confused. Jean-Baptiste also made contact with me — as You well know — but our dialogue never really developed. Now I am beginning to wonder if You and I are going to do any better.

Look, Tom, I know it is not easy. Getting to know me is fraught with obstacles. It is not just the ogre that is looking over Your shoulder. There is something else more insidious. Your ogre only wishes to protect You from being credulous, but inside You is another ogre trying to protect You from something else: self-knowledge. It is the constriction of fear.

Sometimes, it is the ogre of skepticism speaking; at other times, it is the ogre of fear. The former has to do with truth and verification; the latter has to do with reality and well-being. Skepticism is Your academic ogre, and fear is Your existential ogre.

So, You must be careful. Which ogre is speaking? Which one is befuddling You? If You are afraid of recognizing the truth about Yourself, it just may mean that You are afraid of me.

And, if You are, it means You are fearful of Yourself. How can You be sure that it is not the ogre of fear that is behind Your skepticism?

Even so, I am at a loss to understand how You can ask me to tell You about life's beginning when that is precisely what I just finished telling You. Didn't I tell You that all time and space are born in movement, that all movement is born in me, and that the history of the cosmos is my autobiography? Didn't I say that all the jigsaw pieces of the cosmos were neatly in place before the Great Shout and that, after it began, all the pieces were just as interconnected and unified as at the beginning? What changed with the Great Shout was that movement began: I unfolded my being in space and through time, and this unfolding has been so tightly interconnected that, if we could reverse the process, every strand would fold right back into the centrum from which it originated.

More than that, I explained to You that we both share in the ceaseless task of adapting through time and space, and we both do so in such chainlike continuity that our first moment in time remains tightly connected with our present moment.

Furthermore, I gave You the image of a great seed in the center of All, which grew outward into trunk, and branches, and limbs, and twigs. A biological image of cosmic evolution is not merely an analogy. It is the truth of what happened and is still happening. As soon as You looked at me through the eyes of relativity and quantum theory, it became obvious that my process is the prototype of all organic process.

I have told You about these things; inasmuch as You are a clever man, I assumed You would draw the logical conclusion: that the beginning of my life and the beginning of all of life are part of the same story. But that is not the conclusion You drew. Obviously, then, You need more information.

O.K. What can I tell You? Two things, perhaps: life is not an accident. The other is that life is not a necessity. It was neither a fluke, nor was it a preordained plan that life arose in this universe. How does that grab You? But wait! There is a third possibility: that life was an unavoidable event – that its appearance was inevitable.

"But," You are thinking, "how can it be inevitable without being necessary?" The answer to that reveals something about me that will surprise You. It may even disturb You to learn that an awesome secret is concealed at the very core of my being: it is called chance.

What happens when dice are thrown is not at all accidental. It cannot be, since the numbers are already there and the shape of the dice is already there. That means it is already too late for accidents – the numbers and shape of the dice have already tailored the situation.

On the other hand, when the dice are thrown, nothing that happens is determined in advance; it is not necessary that the dice fall in the way they do. We all know that: with any throw of the dice, anything is possible. Even if the same number came up a thousand times in a row, it does not mean that the next throw has to be the same or that it has to be different. The chance is that it could be either.

This does not mean that things happen randomly. Everything in this world has a preset shape and a preestablished momentum, so it is already too late for things to be random. By the same token, it is much too early to tell whether things might be determined by necessity, because anything is possible with the next throw of the dice.

Chance is at the very core of things – indeed, at the very core of my nature. So, when I tell You that it was "inevitable" that life would appear in the cosmos, I mean that, given the rules and preestablished shapes of my jigsaw puzzle, all that was needed was a large outpouring of energy – the Great Shout – and abruptly there was a chance that life would occur.

Atoms have specific shapes, and these shapes allow them to fit together into molecules, just like a precisely fitted jigsaw puzzle. There is nothing accidental about those shapes and the way they fit together.

If You take a few of those atomic shapes – say, a little water, some methane, and ammonia – and mix them all together, then shoot a bit of electrical energy through the mixture, guess what happens? Soon, certain molecules begin to form – amino acids – which are the building blocks for living tissue.

Do You see what I mean? Given the basic shapes and rules, plus a generous gift of energy – for example, the sun – life inevitably occurs. It does not necessarily occur; but, over time, the chance of it is unavoidable.

The odds of this happening by chance are obvious. Let's say that I have something like sextillion stars in my cosmos. That's a lot of stars – take the number one and follow it with twenty-one zeroes. Then let's narrow the odds a bit by saying that, probably, only one of a thousand stars has planets orbiting around it. All right so far? Then let's take it a bit farther by saying that it is also no more than a one-thousand-to-one chance such a star would have one planet that is at such a perfect distance that its temperature is moderate enough for life to occur.

The odds are even more complex. It is also a thousand-to-one chance that such a planet would be large enough to have sufficient gravity to hold an atmosphere around its surface.

We are still not done. What are the chances that such a perfectly situated, perfectly sized planet would have enough carbon, oxygen, hydrogen, and nitrogen to support life? Probably a thousand to one.

Now think about it: sextillion suns are sextillion throws of the cosmic dice. For all You know, that combination could have turned up millions of times; but You are aware that it occurred at least one time: here on Earth in this solar system. You are the living evidence of that chance having inevitably occurred.

When the cosmic dice are thrown 1,000,000,000,000,000,000,000 times, the chances are that the right combination will occur. It will occur neither as an accident, nor as a necessity, but as something that is bound to occur simply because the combination of elements was there from the beginning.

But wait a minute. You were wondering, a short time ago, what gravity had to do with all this. Remember what You were thinking about gravity — that "it didn't appear to account for much"? So, hold onto Your hat, and I'll tell You some things that are obvious to me, but they may be a bit surprising to You.

Keep in mind that my blood is the energy that expands me, and my bone is made of the forces of cohesion. Without the cohesive forces, I would have simply exploded in an instantaneous flash: rather than a Great Shout of beginning, it would have been a Big Bang of short duration. But, happily for me, the constraining hands of cohesion guaranteed that I would maintain my unity and that I would expand in a rather homogeneous fashion — becoming as round as a growing flower.

Among Your physicists, I am known to have four forces of cohesion — four laws: gravity is one of them; electromagnetism is another; and, at the smallest level, the strong force and the weak force that hold together the particles of atoms. These four forces — or laws — of cohesion are the rules of my energetic unfolding. They are, as I said, the bone that gives me form and structure.

There is something very special about these cohesive forces: they did not all come into operation at the same instant. The electromagnetic and weak forces had to wait until things cooled down a bit before they could swing into action and build nuclei. Then another period of time had to pass before things were cool enough to form atoms around the nuclei.

These natural forces of cohesiveness entered the universe in phases, spontaneously springing into action as the cosmos evolved to higher levels of expansion and coolness. Each time they sprang into action, new entities appeared: first, nuclei, then atoms and molecules, then clouds of early galaxies, then stars, then collapsing stars which created new forms of matter, the prerequisite to the next shape that matter was to take: the shape of life – an absolutely unique shape, because the phenomenon of life could only occur if matter imploded upon itself to create an organized process where everything happens from the center outward.

The shape of life created a shape like nothing else in the universe, except one thing: me. The shape of life is, as an organized process, the same shape that the universe has as a whole. It is a replication of the form of the cosmos.

Thus far, not four, but five natural forces have manifested themselves in shaping the entities of the universe. When the time was ripe, the inevitable took place. At the instant that the right combination of material circumstances had finally evolved, a fifth force – or fifth law – spontaneously swirled the atoms into the most extraordinary entity that has ever existed: the soma.

With the appearance of the soma, a ceaselessly moving system of awareness entered the universe. Now hear me carefully. Notice that I didn't say that a "body" came into being. I said "soma." A soma is not a body, but a system of awareness; it came into being in somewhat the way that tornadoes come into being. At first, there is nothing there but colliding winds of different temperatures and pressures. Then, abruptly, a strange shape appears: a dark, vertical entity, spinning and moving about with immense energy and independence.

A tornado is born of the meteorological forces that preceded it and gave it birth. It is, in its origin, merely a product of the conditions that created it. Factually, however, it is a radically different entity: a separate force, moving about freely with its own agenda.

You are not surprised at the specific cause of tornado formation, are You? Neither should You be surprised at the universal

law of somaticization: the fifth natural force of cohesion already
present before the Great Shout and patiently waiting its time
before having the conditions to manifest itself.

A soma is not a body. It is a process of awareness: it senses
the world for its own purposes, and it acts in the world for its
own purposes. Awareness is a sensory-motor process that
actively senses the world and sensorily acts in the world; it is a
process that was already promised, even before the Great Shout.
Make no mistake about it: when the universe came into being,
awareness was coming into being. It was inevitable.

Somas are the flowers that took fifteen billion years of cosmic
nursing to form their buds and bloom. They are my flowering,
and their appearance marked the end of my protracted childhood. When I first saw them sprouting, it was, indeed, like
seeing the forces of the world swirl together to form little
tornadoes – busy systems that spun around a center, moving
quite independently of the original physical forces that spawned
them.

Somas were of the world, evolved out of it, and yet they
were not of the world because there was nothing in the world
like them. If You look at any soma, You see a center surrounded
by forces in movement. It stands out from the surrounding
world, like a universe all to itself.

The somas that flowered in the universe sensed the world
as if they were utterly a part of it, and they moved in the
world as if they were independent of it. Sensing brought the
world into the process. Moving brought the process into the
world. But, between the incoming senses and the outgoing
movements, there was a magic spark. That magic spark,
mediating sensing and doing, was awareness.

Awareness: this was the unique event that occurred with
somas. This is what suddenly flashed outward into the world,
touching everything with its presence. The cosmos was no
longer alone. Out of its womb, the elements were swept together

into a new synthesis. And the result? The universe became aware of itself for the first time.

It took me over fifteen billion years of maturation to gather myself up to the point of leaping into this new dimension of cosmic evolution. When that happened, the cosmos was transformed a second time. The second Great Shout occurred. A second period of expansion and evolution began. A somatic cosmos came into being, and awareness began its evolution.

The very first one-celled somas were aware: they sensed the world, and they moved within it. The evolution of somas has been an evolution of awareness: to sense more of the world and of oneself and to control more of the world and more of oneself.

You, Thomas, being a perspicacious lad, are thinking: "But Fred has already told me that he is the cosmos and that it was his cosmic body that evolved to the point of giving birth to somas. Since that is the case, Fred means that when life occurred for the first time, he became aware for the first time."

Very perspicacious, Thomas! Very perspicacious!

Yours,

Fred

The Scent

When I was a child, wonderful rainstorms visited Waco, Texas, in the spring and early summer. At times, the thunder and lightning were awesome. Towering shafts of electricity, writhing like snakes, would strike downward from the sky; and, abruptly, gigantic crackling sounds exploded into the air, shaking the wooden walls of our house and setting off deep roaring echoes that then billowed back, rattling the walls once more. The air was set vibrating, and I could hear the glasses in the cupboard clinking against one another.

As a boy, I loved those storms. They always came from the north, sweeping down from the flatlands of Oklahoma, Kansas, and the northern plains states, filling my nostrils with the cold, tingling scent of distant Canadian air.

Our house on Parrot Avenue faced north, so I had a full view of the storms from my front porch. One of my earliest memories is of one such summer storm. I was three at the time—perhaps four. The day had been sunny and warm, and I had spent the better part of it playing with Bubba Davis, my best friend who lived in the next block.

We were in my front yard when we noticed the dark, ominous wall coming toward us from the north. To the east, west, and south everything was sunny and undisturbed, but the "norther," as Texans call it, was bearing down on that idyllic calmness with the inexorable stride of doom. It was scary, but exciting.

Bubba and I stopped and watched the norther's steady approach. Gradually, the light diminished, and the neighborhood fell under the grip of a portentous quietness. Everything became hushed—not even the bark of a dog was heard.

Without warning, a chill washed about us, and a little gust of wind buffeted our faces. I shivered. Often, when a norther arrived, the temperature would drop a full ten degrees within a few minutes.

The chill stirring of the air was a harbinger of what was coming. Suddenly, the sun was entirely gone, and a great cowl of darkness was thrown over us. The frame houses and front lawns appeared bleak and threatened.

Within a few seconds, the first drops of rain fell—big drops, cold and heavy. Bubba and I turned our faces upward and opened our mouths. The rain splattered against our brows and cheeks and into our mouths. It was delicious. Our faces and bodies were hot and perspiring from play, and the big, dark droplets fell into our hair and down our necks, cooling our chests.

Then, two blocks away, we saw it coming: the thick curtain of heavy rain bounding toward us like an avalanche. We stood still, fascinated by the approaching roar. When it hit us, we immediately felt drenched. We both turned and ran toward the house and stood under the shelter of the front porch.

Almost as soon as the heavy rain began, we heard an immense rumbling sound lurking just behind it—something deep and gigantic, as if the central powers of the storm were now charging toward us and there were no escape from it.

The first ripping CUURRRACK! burst upon us. The explosion was very near; it seemed to have come down directly over Lasker Avenue, the next street up. We waited, breathlessly, and then the expected, dreaded, hoped-for, ground-shaking BOOOOMMMM! rattled the windows in the front of the house, making the hair stand up on the backs of our necks. Bubba and I opened our mouths and yelled as loudly and as long as we could; then we looked at each other and laughed.

The wind was now tremendous. It whipped and drove the downpour directly into our faces. The CUURRRACK! came again, this time seeming even nearer, and then another crushing BOOOOMMMM! that made my very teeth chatter.

There were two large, wooden porch chairs sitting up against the front of the house. We dragged them over to the center of the porch where the steps came up and turned them upside down, so that the bottoms of the chairs faced toward the storm and the backs were above our heads. The arms of the chairs came around on either side of us, protecting our flanks. The slats in the back of the chairs had wide spaces, and we looked up through them at the onslaught. We crouched inside our magic compartments, meeting the storm head-on.

The roaring darkness now had settled down over Parrot Avenue. The center of the raging wind and rain and rumbling was directly before us. It was aiming for us, bearing down upon us. The CUURR-RACK! was now occurring simultaneously with the nearby lightning as it pounced through the darkness, starkly illuminating the shining streets, the houses across the street, and the bushes on either side of the porch.

We continued to yell, but the storm was so deafening we could scarcely hear ourselves. The rage of the elements was titanic: somehow, it seemed alive. What was happening was not impersonal: the heavings and roarings and flashings seemed inhabited by some being. We were not alone, but were engaged in a grand encounter with an immense and awesome presence.

As the wind and rain blew against the chairs and tore through the wooden slats, we could feel that we were beginning to move and rise—lifting up in our magic compartments and charging into the face of the storm. Our compartments rose, and we soared and blasted into the wind and the sound and into the flashings. Our power was immense, and there was absolutely nothing to harm us. We blasted joyously into the center of it all, laughing and rising higher and higher, indomitable, in full control, without fear, without the least doubt or hesitation, knowing that this was glory—pure glory—and that we were utterly one with it.

Forty years later, I went back to Waco to visit my mother. My father was no longer living, and my mother had moved from Parrot Avenue to Lasker Avenue—only two blocks away from my old home.

Most of those years had been lived far away from the Waco of my childhood. During my infrequent visits home, I fell, automatically, into a state of dreamy nostalgia, as if I were searching Waco for something precious that had been left there. I spent long hours walking around the neighborhood, which now had become almost as faded as my memories of it and of the children who once played there. The neighborhood had become older and worn down. If I had been able to see my former playmates, I would probably have felt the same about them.

While strolling through my old haunts, I would stop and gaze upward at once familiar trees and bushes that were now enormous. I looked at backyard fences that Bubba and I had climbed over. The boards were loose and cracked, hardly capable of holding the weight even of a little boy. I padded through the fields where we had played football and baseball. I strolled through the memories of the kingdom that Bubba and I had once shared.

I visited Dean Highland Elementary School where I had spent six years. When I walked down the corridors that still smelled of the same oil and sawdust they had always used to clean the floors, I discovered that I was unable to see what was there. It was a baffling experience. The flood of remembered images, faces, sounds, and smells crowded to the front of my vision so strongly that I literally could not see what was before my eyes. The halls and rooms and playgrounds were drenched with memory.

My mother thought it curious that I was so concerned to see those old scenes. In our old block on Parrot Avenue, I would walk by Frank Matthew's house on the corner. Frank and my father had spent many weekends fishing on the Bosque River. Their passion for bass was almost mystical.

Next to the Matthews' house was the house of my Aunt Blanche and Uncle Jinx. That had been my second home. Uncle Jinx was then the sports editor of the Waco newspaper. I usually found him sitting at his desk, a cigarette dangling from his lips as his two fingers punched at the typewriter. Aunt Blanche was always busy. She gardened passionately, sewed frenetically, and baked cakes constantly. That made her kitchen a place of endless fascination to young Thomas.

On this particular visit forty years later, I returned home in the late afternoon after a typically long walk. The light was fading, but it was not yet dusk. My mother was in the kitchen, beginning to prepare supper. We talked for awhile. It was summer, and the kitchen door was open.

The late afternoon sun had turned the grass outside a luminous yellow-green. I noticed that the hedges by the kitchen were stirring. My mother sniffed the air and said, "Tommy, I think a norther is coming."

Sure enough, a little puff of coolness came in the door, and, abruptly, it became darker. My mother went over and closed the door, and then continued with the supper.

While she was busy in the kitchen, I went out to the front porch, which was quite small and covered by an aluminum roof. My mother's house on Lasker faced north, just like the old house on Parrot.

I stood, looking northward, and watched the familiar dark wall looming up ahead and steadily approaching the house. The cold wind blew into my face, and then the rain began. I thought of Bubba, wondering what had become of him.

As the rain grew heavier, distant thundering could be heard. Soon, flashes of lightning came into view. The drumming of the rain on the metallic roof was deafening. The air, cool and wet, whipped around my head and blew rain against my shirt. I felt cleansed.

My mother had two metal chairs. I took one and placed it upside down at the front of the porch, just at the edge of the steps. The rain was blowing down against the chair back. I sat down and worked my way under it. The chair gave as little protection as the ones Bubba and I had used. I looked into the storm. It was magnificent. I thought of my mother and, especially, her neighbors—if any of them saw what I was doing, they would suspect I was demented.

The heart of the storm came directly over me, crouching in my magic compartment. The wind, the flashing, the wetness, the booming engulfed me. I headed directly into it, rising to meet it, charging into that gigantic presence without fear.

Then I began to laugh. I had not in the least forgotten the scent of glory.

It had been years since I had thought of these things. When Fred's letter had ended, I continued to sit there—very still and not even thinking. My body was very still. I do not believe I was thinking of anything.

It was during that long moment of quietness that I remembered the two incidents I have just recounted. I spent the rest of the evening just as quietly, pondering what it meant.

The Reverse
of Psychoanalysis

Among other things, the recollections meant a new appreciation of my childhood. Fred's letters were stirring dormant
memories, opening up a channel stretching back to my boyhood.
Forgotten feelings, smells, and visions of an enchanted time of life
flowed toward me through that channel, reconnecting me to the
person I had once been.

It also reconnected me to something precious: my original
sense of the living world. It was a sense of joy—the unreflected joy
of a child who had been happy without being aware of it.

Memories of joy flowed toward me from my boyhood, revivify-
ing feelings of freshness and lightness that had not, I now realized, ceased to exist in my heart. Those feelings had been slowly
smothered under the successive layers of adult life that I had built
up between then and now.

How curious it was that the wisdom I had sought as a philosopher had slipped away from me as I became more sophisticated! I
was beginning to suspect that I had been wiser as a child than as
an adult—but not merely wiser: more joyful. During those earliest
years, I already possessed, somehow, a guiding sense of what was
true and what was right. This was long before I was taught the
adult world's version of what was true and right. I realized that

this was why, during all my adult life, I had remained uncomfortable with what adults claimed to be true and right.

It was becoming obvious that, for me, growing up had been a fall from grace—an inevitable fall, because there was no way to avoid doing so. The adult world was waiting, and I could not prevent becoming an adult. That is what acculturation had been for me: an adulteration. It had not led me either to joy or wisdom.

Learning to become an adult had taken me away from the happy sensitivities of boyhood, covering them over with the tough second skin of caution and responsibility. I had learned to turn my attention from affirming the world to defending against it. That was what adulthood had taught me.

As I now realized, adulteration had moved the locus of my experience from "here" to "there." Rather than feeling reality as being "mine," reality had become something outside of me. Reality was not something I possessed, but something that possessed me. Fred's insistence that I think of him as "here"—rather than "there"—seemed directly connected with the resurrection of my childhood memories.

But, unfortunately, I could not help being an adult. It was already too late. The second skin stood between me and the world, protecting me against its ever-threatening thereness, making me cautious and self-conscious. It was too late to forget all the things I had learned in the process of becoming an adult. The learning was encrusted around me. To give up adulthood would be to give up my identity—even my sanity.

Something else was possible: adulthood might be capable of redemption. It was not a question of forgetting or denying what I had learned; rather, it was a question of realigning myself with the fresh breezes of forgotten beauty that had been my first experience of life.

I could see that, under Fred's guidance, I was undergoing the reverse of what takes place in psychoanalysis. Rather than making me conscious of the unhappy memories that growing up had repressed, I was becoming conscious of the happy memories that adulthood had repressed. I liked that. It was like being reminded that everything is "all right" after all—just as Johnny Hines' song had said. I had just forgotten that this had always been the case.

I also pondered the meaning of Fred's words, "Very perspicacious, Thomas!" As far as I could I figure out, this meant that Fred did not possess awareness until life evolved out of the cosmos. It was as if Fred's cosmic body had to mature to the point of developing awareness.

Another thing I pondered that evening was the way Fred capitalized "You." My first take was wrong: he was not doing this for honorific reasons, as if he thought more highly of me than of himself. He was doing it, because he was not merely addressing me, but was speaking to everyone else: when he said "You," he meant "You, the human."

On second thought, I may not have been completely wrong on my first take. Each time he said "You," it seemed to mean "You humans who do not think as highly of Yourselves as I do." In fact, I was certain this was what he meant.

Bee Dance

One Sunday, I went down to Fort Baker, a decommisioned army base whose buildings were now being used as studios for San Francisco area artists—painters, sculptors, and dancers.

A friend had invited me to an unusual dance program. We arrived to find a small crowd milling about in front of a two-story building that had once served as a recreation center. There had been a bowling alley on the first floor and a basketball court on the second floor.

A young man emerged from the building and spoke to the crowd. He said that the building we were about to enter had been abandoned for over a decade and that during those years the entire structure had become a gigantic beehive. I gazed down one side of the building and saw hundreds of bees pouring through an open window on the second floor. Others were also watching the dark, buzzing stream of brown-yellow bodies, perhaps wondering if they wanted to enter the formerly abandoned building.

The young man then opened the door, allowing the group of a hundred or so people to enter the building. We went into the bowling alley and stood, waiting for things to be ready upstairs where the program was to take place.

The first floor was eerie. In the gutters of the bowling alleys were, literally, hundreds of thousands of carcasses of dead bees. On the ledges of the windows were other piles of bee carcasses, as light as air. Above these tiny bodies were scores of live bees repeatedly climbing up the windowpanes, futilely attempting to get outside. No windows were open downstairs. So I surmised that the only window in and out of the building was the open one I had seen outside on the second floor. Some of the bees had wandered downstairs, becoming trapped—thus, the thousands of little carcasses.

A few minutes later, we were invited upstairs. As the crowd slowly filed upward on the narrow wooden staircase, they were met at the top by a young woman who gave each of them a small glass jar of honey.

Carrying our gifts of amber sweetness, we walked into the large open room, which formerly had been a basketball court. In the middle of the court hung an immense scrim, separating our half of the room from the back half. Everyone was asked to sit down on the floor in front of the scrim. On the other side of the scrim, which protected us from the bees, were seven huge stacks of beehives, looking like little skyscrapers. The hives were on the left side of the room; on the right side, some boxes stood against the wall.

The tall windows on either side were covered over with a dark yellow substance. The sun coming through the windows filled the room with a vibrant light. After a moment, I realized that the light was the color of honey.

Later, I found out that the windows were covered over with huge sheets of beeswax. The air was heavy with its honeyed odor. Only one window had an opening—a large, round hole in the beeswax, through which streamed an intense shaft of sunlight. The beam of sunlight was alive with tiny streaks: bees were entering the window like bullets and darting down the stream of light, heading for the hives. Other bees, leaving the hives, were darting up the same stream and disappearing out the window. The room vibrated with a thousand buzzings, and the bees wove a shimmering garland around the glowing beam.

When my eyes adjusted to the dimmer corners of the room, I saw on the left, near the scrim, a rocking chair. A man was sitting there, motionless. He was wearing a hat. For five minutes, he sat, while we watched and listened to the comings and goings of the bees as they moved along the garlanded sunbeam.

The man began to move. He slowly stood, picked up an odd-looking metal teapot, and opened the lid. He proceeded to stuff the pot with what looked like dried leaves and pieces of burlap. Having filled the little pot, he took a match, lit the materials he had stuffed inside, and replaced the lid. Heavy puffs of smoke came from the spout.

Picking up the pot, the man carried it over to one of the stacks of beehives. The hive was swarming with little bees. He put the spout of the pot into the holes in the sides of the hive, gradually filling it with smoke. This was to quiet the bees so that he could open up the hive.

He lifted off the top section of the first hive and set it on the ground. Next, he proceeded to take off the second section of the hive. Then, the third. Occasionally, he stopped and injected more smoke into the holes. Soon, the entire hive was dismantled. He checked its contents for honey. Then, satisfied with what he had seen, he slowly replaced each section of the hive, so that it stood tall again.

The next hive was even taller. The beekeeper injected the smoke and began dismantling the second hive, inspecting it. This went on for almost ten minutes. It was done so slowly that the effect was hypnotic.

Then he came to a third hive. It was taller than he was. He put the smoke pot into the holes and began removing each segment of the hive. But when he removed the second segment, I saw something astonishing. There was a human being standing inside, the head wrapped around with a cloth. Only the back of the head showed. He removed another segment, and then you could see the shoulders and upper trunk, similarly wrapped. The cloth was the color of a bee.

When the last of the segments was removed, a young woman stood there, tall and enigmatic, turning her head so that the face could be seen. Her body and face were covered with bees. She, however, barely moved. Everything was dreamlike in slowness.

She stepped out of the hive and moved toward the scrim, hesitantly, as if searching for something. She moved like a just-born bee. Then she stopped, and began crouching forward, reaching down and rubbing her hands against her sides. She was practicing the action of gathering pollen. She moved in front of the hives, then between them, and around them. She seemed restless, seeking something.

Later, she was drawn toward the beam of light, festooned with hundreds of bees. She reached up to the window, trying to escape. I suddenly thought of the thousands of bee carcasses in the bowling alley below and the frantic bees throwing their bodies against the windowpane, seeking the light.

She reached up to the window, pressing her body against it, longing for escape, vainly seeking a way out. She was trapped inside, while multitudes of bees soared through the hole in the window and out into freedom. She stopped, returned to the middle of the room, and became quite still, as if deliberating. The moment of deliberation lasted a full minute. Abruptly, her head turned toward the windows on the opposite side of the room. She darted across the floor, leaped up on a box, crashed through the second-floor window, and disappeared. There was silence, punctuated by the droning buzz. The gaping sheet of beeswax stood open, marking the passage of her body and showing a fair, blue sky outside. She was gone. She was free.

Nobody moved. They were mesmerized. The beekeeper sat quietly in his rocking chair, the buzzing continued to saturate the honeyed air, and the sunlight of a pristine summer's day beamed down through the window. It was, perhaps, five minutes before people quietly began to get up and leave.

I stepped outside into the sunlight, sniffing the cool air blowing in off the nearby ocean. I looked at the right side of the building where she had broken through the window. A small platform had been built by the window for the dancer to land on when she had shattered the sheet of beeswax. A ladder leaned against the building.

My friend and I ambled down toward the beach. We sat down on the sand. I opened my jar of honey. She stuck her finger in and tasted it. I did the same. I had seen the bees, smelled the beeswax, seen the honeyed light, and now I was, finally, tasting the honey. The experience was now complete.

I thought about the bee dance. It seemed to be about freedom—about moving freely and not being confined. I looked up at the empty blue of the sky. Within the dark confines of the bee-hive room, the gaping hole left in the sheet of beeswax had shown the tiniest segment of this same blue. Yet that small patch of fair sky had seemed immense.

The openness of the sky was an invitation to freedom. Freedom is not simply an escape—that is only the beginning. Freedom is a way of living where the inner being can act without restriction. Freedom is far more than an abstract legal concept; it is a state of being where everything is functioning optimally.

The dance reminded me that freedom is a human need, as genetically fixed as a bee's. Freedom is not merely a negative state of "no restrictions outside." It is a positive state of using oneself fully—it is an inner state requiring skill and discipline.

You have to be sensitive to be free. Also, you have to be smart. And you have to be alert. You have to have reliable knowledge. In general, you have to be fluidly adaptive. The soul must be supple and as open as the sky.

Living freely means to flow forward into the world with the least effort and the least expenditure of energy, like a surfer gracefully adapting to the force of the wave and surging along—or, like a little boy in a magic compartment rising upward into a sky that is open and unrestricting even in the midst of storm.

Fred was getting to me. I sat on the sand, aware that I would not have reacted to the bee dance in this way, except for Fred. The cool breeze moved around my body. Gulls and pelicans sailed across the sky. The ocean flashed and shimmered. All was moving.

At that moment, I felt that all time, space, and reality could be summed up in two words: things moving.

No. Three words: things moving freely.

A Question
of Faith

From Monday till Saturday, I stayed away from the yellow pad. I needed time to assimilate the extraordinary things Fred had told me. I knew how serpents must feel after swallowing an entire animal—they remain still for a long time until digestion has taken place.

My mind went blank for the week. I avoided thinking about the Second Great Shout. It was simply too much to handle. The idea that cosmic evolution moved inevitably into somatic evolution was so compelling that I felt a kind of breathlessness at the very thought of it. The notion that the genuine evolutionary event was not merely of body types and functions—but of awareness—that thought totally baffled me. Since I did not know what to think about it, I did not think at all.

I was fallow that week, but in other respects wonderful things were happening. For one thing, the work with my clients had never been better. I was more sensitive. The fact that I was becoming more aware of myself seemed to transfer directly to my clients. Again, it was a toss-up between saying that I was more *aware* of their bodies or aware of *more* of their bodies.

What had happened was that I no longer felt I was touching their "bodies." Rather, I was touching individual systems of movement and sensitivity. I was touching what Fred called "somas."

So my touch became more subtle. In fact, the gentler my touch, the more aware of my client I became, and the more aware the client was of me. An interchange was taking place at a deeper level—a lively communication between myself as a soma and my client as a soma. It was not my intelligence that was sharper, but my sensitivity.

I did the best work of my career that week. Beyond that, I simply felt better, and I think it showed in my relations with others: everything went smoothly and without conflict. In general, more was happening in my life.

It was strange: I felt I was growing—but how does a man in his fifties "grow"? Although I really did not know the answer, it was certainly happening. It was the same feeling of growing and expanding I had had as a child—the child with whom I was, once again, making contact. That made perfectly good sense: to contact one's childhood again must mean to begin growing again.

It was exhilarating. Things were on the move. I felt like Samuel Beckett's Vladimir who, sensing that Godot was finally arriving, cries out: "Time flows again already." For me, time had finally sprung loose and was flowing freely again.

As the boy and man drew closer together, I felt whole again. The pieces of my life seemed to be coming together, as if I had been dismembered and now I was re-membering myself. I liked that: remembering my boyhood was re-membering myself.

So, I wasn't really fallow that week—just the opposite. During the next five evenings, while at my desk editing *Somatics* magazine, I resolutely ignored the tall, thin line of yellow paper glowing between the brown of the wood and the dark leather binding of the Ueberweg book. Nevertheless, in the back of my mind was the glowing question: "How could awareness 'evolve'?"

I maintained my patience until Saturday. Late that morning, I took the yellow pad from the shelf and laid it upon my desk. A tremendous eagerness seized me as the protracted period of anticipation seemed about to end.

I waited a few moments until I felt calmer. As always, my greatest fear was that I might say the wrong thing. I could not risk offending Fred another time.

Finally, I picked up a pen and wrote the following:

Dear Fred:
    Tell me how awareness evolved.

Yours,
Tom

Blessedly, there was no onrush of shock or anger. In fact, there was no pause at all. My pen skipped a line and wrote the following:

Dear Tom:

    Let me begin by quoting a philosopher who recently said that "all time, space, and reality could be summed up in three words: things moving freely." That was You, of course, with a bee in Your bonnet. I do believe You are beginning to tune into my wavelength.

    "Things moving freely" . . . what a felicitous phrase! It has a fair ring to it, and it expresses what is really going on. It was that way one second after the Great Shout, and it continues to be that way at this very moment. The energy that exploded my jigsaw pieces into the void is still moving things outward just as fast now, fifteen billion years later, as it did at the beginning. All those pieces are expanding outward into a limitless void — freely.

    It is quite a scene — reality is bracketed by an infinity of empty space, and a good thing it is because otherwise I would not have any room for expansion, would I? My cosmic body is growing outward freely into an infinite frontier, without restriction — just like a bee bursting outward into the open sky.

    The bee and I are much alike. To tell You the truth, all living things are like me. They are replicas of me. I am constantly moving forward; so are they. I have many pieces organized in a single process; so do they. *Everything within me is interconnected with everything else, as an integrated whole; so are they. Most important of all: from the very beginning my cosmic process poured forth from the center outward, just as Yours does. What a lovely* imago dei *You are.*

Organisms are replicas of my organic nature – they are just as coherent, as forward moving, as interconnected, and as centered as I am. It's no surprise that I am their prototype, since there was really nothing else for them to evolve from other than my puzzle pieces.

But the Earth – that's a most special piece of the evolved jig-saw puzzle. It is, You might say, my womb, and it grew right along with the rest of my cosmic body, pregnant from its beginning with the expectation of a Second Great Shout. When the first somas emerged from the Earth's flesh, my reason for being was revealed: to become aware – to sense myself and the world, to move myself and the world.

Thomas, hold Your pen carefully. Do not make any slips, because I am going to tell You a wonderful secret. I have berated You several times about not knowing who You are. Sorry about that. Now, I can be more positive. To the question, "Who are You?" there is an answer, a very clear one, and it is this: "You are awareness." Isn't that obvious? The burning center of Your being is awareness – something that took fifteen billion years to evolve. Quite an investment of time, if I may say so! It was worth every second of it.

Be assured that awareness is not merely a human trait; it is the nature of all living things to be aware. Bees are aware – they know where they want to go. Flowers are aware, trees are aware, grasses are aware – they all know where the sun is, and they all turn toward it. All living creatures are centers of awareness. The earth is covered with awareness. It is alive with an active sentience, having a million forms and directions.

All these creatures sense themselves and the world while, simultaneously, moving themselves and the world. Flowers move toward the sun because they can sense it – and so they can sense it. They sense the sun because they can move toward it – and so they can move toward it.

I hope that's not too difficult for You. Humans have a bad habit of separating sensing from moving; they err in believing that knowing is separate from doing. But, in living beings, sensing and moving are the same thing. You cannot look at something without moving and focusing Your eyes. Correct? So, which is looking? Passive or active? Of course, it is both. And that is what awareness is: a system that simultaneously receives the world into itself and moves itself into the world.

If I wanted to be a bit crude, I might say that awareness is like a mouth moving forward. It is like eating. And do You know what awareness consumes? Experience – that's what. Experience is the food of that insatiable hunger. Fifteen billion years went by before experience came into existence. Now it is everywhere, covering the Earth. At this moment, You are experiencing, the crows up on the hill are experiencing, as are the deer, the quail, and Your plum trees. Their experience is of many different kinds and dimensions, but it is all the same: they are centers of awareness, actively creating their experience by a sensory-motor process.

Keep that last sentence in mind, Thomas. It lets You know– who all of You are. And keep Your mouth open. There is more coming – just what You have been fidgeting about all week: the "glowing question."

When the time was ripe, the fifth universal law of cohesiveness imploded matter into a centralized process of awareness. That was the Second Great Shout. By that, I mean the second beginning. At that moment, cosmic evolution peaked; its long travail was crowned. The fruit of fifteen billion years had ripened. From that time onward, the cosmic tree, having borne its fruit, continued its own plodding march onward toward entropy, but cosmic evolution had, at this juncture, ceased to be the most interesting thing happening.

Now the real beginning occurred — the true creation. The cosmos had given birth to something truly interesting, for something was happening that was both new and unpredictable. The variety of forms created by cosmic evolution was as nothing compared to the variety of forms that began to appear through somatic evolution. For me, it was as if my childhood had ended and I could move into the excitement of adolescence.

Once the implosive event of life began its expansion, varieties of awareness spread like wildfire over this planet. The Earth glowed like a giant sentient bouquet in the midst of the universe. Millions of species of life spewed forth, giving spectacular evidence that the Second Great Shout was a shifting of gears upward. Everything speeded up in this terrestrial arena of the cosmos. Newness abounded; growth became the shining new theme of space and time.

Because at Your core You are awareness, You can easily figure out how it was that awareness evolved. It evolved from fixed sensory-motor patterns to unfixed patterns. It evolved from automatic, unlearned patterns to voluntary, learned patterns. It evolved from predictability to unpredictability. It evolved from rigidity to freedom. The earliest life forms were robotic and predictable. They had strict limits to what they could sense and what they could do. Spiders spin webs of exactly the same number of strands, just as ants forage in an identical manner. The simplest life forms are predictable. The complex creatures, like the vertebrates and especially the mammals, were less fixed and limited. They were freer and more unpredictable.

Ah! There's that word again: freedom. "Things moving freely." I move freely. I expand outward into the void with no resistance whatsoever. That is my given state of freedom. You, my imago dei, *and all Your fellow awarenesses are evolving* toward the same state. You are compelled to because it's the easiest way to go — like water flowing downhill, it is the way of least entropy.

Do You want me to spell it out? Do You want to know the underlying bass note of evolution? Listen. Can't You hear it? It is the persistent passacaglia of freedom, and I am sure that it does not surprise You, inasmuch as your awareness has been haunted by that sound since Your own beginnings. The ultimate thrust of my own destiny is to move into freedom — into the vast frontier of the void — so You can be sure that if I, Your progenitor, am impelled in that direction, so are You.

The evolution of life forms has been from unlearned programs of automatic reflexes to something quite different: learned ways of seeing and doing. You do not have to teach a doodlebug how to walk; it already knows. The learning is already there in the genes. For that matter, You do not teach a just-born colt to walk. Imagine that: four long spindly legs to coordinate, and it gets up on them and somehow knows what to do. That is wonderful to behold.

What is even more wonderful is learning how to walk. What could You do when You were born? Walk? Talk? Put on Your breeches? You couldn't do any of those things. What an inept little clod You were. In time, You learned to walk and to talk and to dress Yourself — primarily because somebody else took care of You during Your early ineptitude and taught You these things.

That is when awareness and greater adaptability hit their stride: with mammals and the delightful contrivance of loving parentage. It is parental care that allows time for creatures of learning to piece together their awareness of themselves and their world. The evolution from fixed behavior to free behavior happened only because of a special social event: the family.

Now that is a remarkable thing, when You think about it: freedom evolved as families evolved. None of You have quite *grasped the importance of the biological fact that freedom is the result of a social arrangement. It is not an individual event. It is a social event. There can be freedom only in society — not apart from it.*

In mammals, the parental reflexes to care for the newborn allow the newborn time to learn. And once You learn to do something, You can either do it or not do it, depending on the situation. That is choice. That is freedom.

That is why You feel closer to bears and bunnies than You do to doodlebugs and dung beetles. Bears and bunnies have parental nurturing, just as You do; and so they learn to behave a little more like You do. Doodlebugs have a tiny capacity to learn as well. Just-born colts have an even greater capacity. In fact, all somas have that capacity, implanted within them during the original implosion. It just took time for it evolve.

So, You see how it has worked out: the most helpless and dependent of all newly born creatures — namely, humans — are the ones most talented at learning. That is why humans are the creatures most capable of being free.

Thomas, I am saying this quickly, so that You do not have a chance to feel stuffed like a serpent. Later, You can do Your digesting. Right now, I want You to sense the sweep of things. And I do not want You to forget Your question, which was about awareness. Since awareness is what You wanted to know about, that is where this discussion is still heading.

To be aware is to experience oneself and one's world. It is an ongoing process — simultaneously sensing and acting — which I crudely suggested is like a ceaseless consumption of the world. But think about that for a minute: a center of awareness experiencing a world is a "here" experiencing a "there."

Oho! I slipped up on You with that one. Suddenly, we are back to square one: "Dear Fred: Are you there?" And what did I say? "No."

I was telling You the truth, which is what I always tell You, whether or not You are prepared to digest it; however, at this point, Your digestion has improved. If You look for the ultimate out "there," You will never find it. The observed universe is, finally, an irreducible mystery – a jigsaw puzzle without all of the pieces. Do You know the reason? It is because the ultimate meaning of the universe is not "there," but "here." It ceased to be "there" after the Second Great Shout. The ultimate is "here."

But where is "here"? "Here" is where awareness is. That is where You will find me. My whole being is invested in aware-ness. The rest of it – the continued expansion of my cosmic body – is a matter of utter indifference to me. That is not where the action is.

Can't You see my predicament? I have no "here." I am, liter-ally, nowhere. I exist in a void, but there has evolved within me this marvelous, precious event called awareness, *which is not me, but You. I have no awareness except through You. I was unawakened until You came along. I was a no-mindedness moving in nothingness – but now, with You and Your hungry awareness, I have become something. I am evolving. With Your presence, a point of view – a Hereness – has entered the relativ-ity of my far-flung system. Only with Hereness can there be Thereness. Only a center of awareness can experience a world.*

O.K. Get Your paddle ready now. We are approaching the rapids. It is what You have been looking forward to, but I do not want You to hit the rocks and overturn.

The evolution of awareness You want to know about is an evolution of the sensory-motor process toward greater learning and freedom, toward a wider range of sensing and acting, toward a bigger "here" and a bigger "there." The size of the latter depends on the size of the former. (Can You hear the rapids?)

What You would experience as reality if You were a doodle-bug is not the same as the reality You experience now, which is immensely vaster and deeper. Your abilities of experiencing reality are still growing and evolving. They have just gotten started.

Listen carefully. Do not let the noise of the rapids drown out the sound of my voice. Reality is not something out "there," fixed and settled. Reality is learned. Reality radiates outward from Your center. It always has. From the instant that life and awareness appeared on this Earth, reality was created by Hereness.

What You experience as reality is what You have learned in the course of growing up. It is no more than that: Your acculturation. It is what has simultaneously defined and limited Your experience, befouling Your awareness. Because each of You is a center of awareness, each of You has his own reality — according to what You have learned. From culture to culture and from individual to individual, the range of experienced realities is immense.

What You experienced as reality at one year of age is not at all the reality You knew at five, and what You took to be the real world at thirteen is not what You knew it to be when You were twenty. At each stage, You redefined reality, realizing the limitations of Your prior experience of reality. You know this already in Your own life, so draw the conclusion. Do not be afraid to risk the rapids: reality is evolving.

The pace of reality's evolution is totally dependent upon the degree that human individuals can grow beyond what they were originally taught reality to be. Do You remember about the egg and the first persona? The reality that humans experience is always infinitely smaller and meaner than the one that awaits them. You can enter that larger reality: first, by breaking out of the shell of Your original learning; and then, secondly, by bursting out of the shell of what, at this very moment, You believe to be real. That is how reality evolves: by expecting that the limits You experience and live in today will not be the reality You will experience and live in tomorrow – by freely intending it.

Listen, Tom, what humans really are – and what the world really is – has never been anything other than a belief that has its roots solely in individual experience. It is not a fact out "there," but a temporary belief that You hold "here" about what is out "there."

With the advent of humans, evolution was no longer by natural selection, but by intentional selection. The gears shifted upward into the realm of freedom. What the real, practical world shall be is totally up to You. Reality, You see, is not something fixed, any more than it is something out "there." Reality is experience. It is ongoing. It is right now.

So the question is: how shall You experience Yourself and Your world today and every day? What are Your real limits? What are Your real powers? What are the possibilities of the world? How healthy are You? How intelligent are You? How loving can You be? How beautiful are You?

Don't You realize that there is literally no answer to these questions other than what You intend the answer to be – what You absolutely believe and insist and expect it to be? Don't You realize that if You have absolute faith in what You intend and expect, it really becomes the case – it becomes absolutely and practicably real?

Don't You realize that the possible combinations of real information Your brain's cells are capable of storing are greater than the number of elementary particles of the universe itself? Don't You realize that the ultimate limits of the human brain and human reality are larger than the cosmos itself? This is just as obvious as is the fact that the ultimate destiny of my being will be far larger than my present being.

Don't You get the point? Don't You see why the urge of freedom is such an inescapable and haunting presence in Your experience? Don't You understand, now, that all You need to do *is* use it? *At that moment, You set foot in the Fair Realm — a place that is very near.*

Thomas, You must have faith in the creator — absolute faith. The theologians were right about that. They only made the error of misplacing that faith: in the "there" rather than the "here." The faith necessary to save both the world and Your soul is "here" in Yourself.

That is all I ask of You — not to have faith in me, but to have faith in Yourself.

All right, Thomas. It is now time for digestion.

Yours,

Fred

Help from the *O.E.D.*

I was awakened at daybreak the next morning by the sound of crows. I lay still, floating in a half-awake, half-asleep reverie — what psychologists call a hypnopompic state. I often do my best thinking during such early morning moments.

As my mind opened to wakefulness, two words were there, waiting for me: "Fair Realm." Once again, Fred had deposited a giant nugget on my long, yellow pad, and now it lay inside my head.

He had been leading me up to it, preparing me for it, just as he had done with all the other things he had sprung on me. The word "fair" had been scattered around, here and there, in his recent communications. I could not help noticing it, because I was not sure what it meant. I knew about "fair balls" and "foul balls," and about "playing fair." I knew about "fair damsels" and "fair skies," but I could not see the common connection between them.

I kept turning the puzzle over. A baseball could be hit "fair" or "foul." O.K., that meant the ball was either in the field of play or not. But how did that relate to someone being "fair" in his dealings with someone else, or about damsels being "fair"?

Either Fred was talking nonsense — and I knew better than that — or the word was much more ancient and complex than I had realized. The Australians, I remembered, have the term "fair dinkum," but they hardly use it anymore.

"Fair" was a dead word. Almost an archaic word. Yet Fred insisted on using it.

The more I turned the matter over, the more I ceased to be in a reverie. It was aggravating to think I had heard this word all my life without ever really understanding it. There was only one thing to do: look it up in the big *Oxford English Dictionary*—my court of last resort when I was confused about a word.

I put on my slippers, walked down the hall, went through the kitchen and out the door, across the patio, and into my study. I pulled out the huge volumes where the *R's* and *F's* were and laid them on my desk. I looked up two words: "realm" and "fair." I figured that "realm" was derived from the same root as "royal," and I was right. A "realm" was a kingdom: a place where one exercised power.

O.K. The first part was easy. But what was the derivation of "fair"?

It turned out to be a formidable word. I could not believe what I saw: two and a half pages were devoted to "fair." The first thing I learned was that its earliest meaning was in antithesis to "foul."

I stopped and looked up "foul." Another surprise: it took up two pages. "Foul" was anything grossly offensive to the senses of smell or sight: something rotten. It also meant the opposite of "clean": "covered with dirt." "Foul" handwriting was blotted and illegible. It also meant "clogged up" or "encumbered with a foreign substance." That was interesting. Moral and spiritual pollution was also foul. It meant "ugly" and "disfigured," as opposed to "beautiful" and "fair"; and it meant, as well, "contrary to the rule," as in baseball, when a ball is hit foul or fair. Finally, it meant "unfavorable" or "harsh" weather, as opposed to "fair" weather.

At this point, I lined up the contraries: "foul" was to "fair" as "dirty" to "clean," "ugly" to "beautiful," "within the rules" to "outside the rules," and "unfavorable" weather to "clear" weather.

"Fair" had a number of meanings other than its ancient use as the opposite of "foul." It meant "light," instead of "dark," and also "daylight." A thing was "fair" when it was unblemished, unstained, smooth. A "fair" action was equitable and right. It also had the attendant meanings of "open," "unbiased," "benign," "successful," "gentle," "peaceable," and "easy."

What an extraordinary word! I was astonished at the variety of meanings, all of which connoted good and desirable things. And I was embarrassed to think that so important a word was almost unknown to me. I rarely used it, nor did anyone else. It was a word which—significantly, I felt—had almost disappeared from the English language.

Surely, a word whose basic meaning could be applied to so many different circumstances was a profound word—the kind of word usually picked up by philosophers to designate something fundamental or ultimate.

Yet, to my knowledge, it was a word totally absent from the vocabulary of philosophers. They had ignored it. For that matter, neither was it a word used by theologians. The two "profound" disciplines, philosophy and theology, had nothing to do with this word of such profundity.

I tried to put Fred's two words together. A "fair realm" would be a place where one exercised power—in effect, a kingdom. And this kingdom would be a place of light, openness, cleanness, clearness, and it would be a place of beauty. A "fair realm" was a kingdom that was right and equitable—one staying within the rules. It was a realm unblemished and unstained, which implied that it was purely and genuinely itself, just as it was designed to be. A "fair realm" was unencumbered and unrestricted—a fact that allowed it to be successful as well as smooth, gentle, easy, and peaceable.

Fred wrote that I had "befouled" my awareness. He meant that, in growing up into adulthood, my awareness had become "disfigured" and pushed out of its given shape. A befouled awareness was "dirty" and "rotten"; it smelled rotten, and it offended the eyes. Such an awareness operated "contrary to the rule"; it was "biased," "wrong," "closed," "harsh," "criminal," "unsuccessful," and "without peace." It was an ugly awareness, and it functioned in darkness.

Fred was talking about a situation in which, like a king in his domain, one is able to act freely. This state of freedom brought with it clarity, rightness, beauty, genuineness, success, light, gentleness, and peace.

Another thing. He said the Fair Realm was "near," which meant that it was an attainable state—near enough that, perhaps, I myself might attain it during my lifetime. But attain *what*? Did he mean a state of awareness—a way of experiencing reality? Could a state of awareness bring along with it clarity, rightness, beauty, and all the rest? Fred was urging me toward such a state, but how was I supposed to get into it? By simply wanting to? That could not be. You do not just jump into a new state of awareness. Was it supposed to happen by remembering my childhood? Or by becoming more childlike? But I could not do that. I certainly could not become childlike again. That was impossible: it was too late.

Suddenly, I stopped. Where, I asked myself, did the idea of "too late" come from? What *inside* of me immediately insisted that it was impossible?

I had caught myself! I had caught the ogre that was actively holding me back—the "baffle" that prevented me from fully understanding the answers Fred gave me. I now knew what it meant to "understand" what Fred said. It meant to experience it, to make it part of my ongoing awareness: but at the very moment of my movement toward understanding, the "too late," instantly asserted itself. It was a reflex action—as natural as blinking.

That reflex was my ogre—and something else! It was the sign of my "befoulment"—the baffle of my awareness, defending the reality in which I had settled. How wretched that I could have the prodigious experience of being in direct contact with Fred and, in response, automatically judge him to be wrong. How disfigured and clogged up I must be to think that what he said might apply to someone else "there" in the world, but not to me "here." The ogre was telling me that I knew better, that Fred was not to be believed.

How rotten of me. Yes, that was the word. But that was just the point: what I had thought to be the case was not the case—who I thought I was, was not who I really was. Once the innocence of my childhood had fallen away from me, I had become smeared with the learning of the presumed "real" world. And the result: an ugly awareness, functioning in darkness.

That was the situation in Dostoevski's *Brothers Karamazov,* in the story of Christ's return to Earth. The Grand Inquisitor, representing the holy wisdom of humankind, rejected God the Son in proclaiming the absolute limits of the human soul. God the Son was to be rejected in the name of human limitation. The Grand Inquisitor was the personification of my ogre.

Even so, the ogre was not I. The ogre was the voice of the cultural past, fixed into my soul like something unchangeably "there"—a voice urging me not to risk being other than what I am, not to consider the possibility of reality being other than what it is.

There again, I felt another, even deeper bafflement. How can reality be different from what it is? It is what it is, isn't it? How can my awareness change what is? I wanted to believe Fred, but I could not understand him.

The deeper problem was that Fred was saying I could actually and practically change what is. He did not mean hallucinating such a change—by going into a subjective fantasy where I idiotically assume the impossible, flap my wings three times, then jump off the roof and kill myself, madly experiencing the whole fiasco as an instant flight to heaven.

No, Fred clearly did not mean that "it is all in Your mind." He meant *really* changing reality, but if we could *will* reality into being, it would be like alchemy—a kind of magic. It would be the subjective human equivalent of discovering that matter was only another form of energy and that energy is nothing more than what matter would be if it spread itself out to the tune of light: $E = MC^2$.

Is that what Fred was trying to get through my thick skull? My eyes hovered over the *O.E.D.*, scanning the many meanings of "fair," trying to intuit the common root that would make sense of it and turn my darkness into light. I knew that the coalescence of those meanings was within me. It was "here." The meaning of the Fair Realm was "here," very, very near.

It occurred to me that what I was struggling with might, indeed, be exactly the same baffling struggle that twentieth century physicists went through when they were trying to come to terms with the incredible fact of relativity and quantum physics. The data did not make sense. The evidence pointed to conclusions which were impossible. The data could *not* be right, because they contradicted what physicists knew to be the case about reality. Yet the evidence came from reality—it really *was* the case.

The physicists were faced with a paradox. If their conclusions were true, then everything we had previously thought to be solid and certain about our world had to be revamped. If their conclusions were valid, a whole new realm of possibilities opened before them—practical possibilities, which would literally transform our lives.

A new realm of possibilities. A "realm." The suspicion began to form in me that the quantum realm was the discovery of the crucial secret of Thereness—the objective, third-person universe. The Fair Realm that Fred was speaking about was the crucial secret of Hereness—the subjective, first-person universe of human awareness.

A Fine
Conundrum

I was lying on the chaise. The noonday sun drenched the patio, warming my skin against the coolish breeze that was sweeping down my little valley.

It was my midday break. I had skipped rope for ten minutes, then had my lunch. There were still forty-five minutes before I had to shower and return to my clients.

I thought of the earlier time on the patio when I lay there wrestling with the problem of the yellow pad, the sweat stinging my vision and the round ball of the sun prying its way through my eyelids. It had been an insistent sun — a burning sun of revelations and searching, its radiance full of questions.

The period of questions had now yielded to a new period: one of answers. I had, it seemed, begun to tune into Fred's wavelength. At least, that is what he had said. Even so, the answers were hardly self-evident. Fred's answers left me hanging in the same way his questions did. Everything he had written during the course of these summer weeks had the effect of driving me more and more back into myself. Still, that was what he had already told me about religiousness: it had to do with unanswerable questions — with perennial problems that could never be resolved, but could only be lived with.

Now, several weeks later, it was a different sun. It was a different patio. It was a different valley, down which the cool breeze blew. The earth itself was different, and I was different from the man I had been a few weeks earlier.

A surge of air shook the bamboo chimes, making a soft clattering. Then the wind paused momentarily; in the stillness I heard another sound—softer and thinner, like a tiny scratching. It came from somewhere just behind me. I lay still, listening carefully as the tiny sound came nearer.

Then, it was right beside me, on my right. Out of the corner of my eye I saw two small heads bobbing fore and aft. I kept very still. It was the quail. I shifted my head slowly, so I could look directly at them: one was a male, with the high coxscomb and vigilant strut; the other, a female, with softer coloring, looking carefully left and right as she scurried along.

They were incredibly beautiful. I had never had the chance to see quail up close. There was a wonderful stateliness in the way they moved. But there was something else: behind them were eight tiny babies, freckled and big-eyed, scampering along on toothpick legs, heads bobbing up and down as they searched for food on the patio.

It was a grand procession. I felt privileged to be so near to creatures of such preciousness. They continued onward, slowly making their way to the other end of the patio, veering left toward the juniper bushes, gradually pecking their way into the enfolding shadows, then disappearing.

Little "somas" passing by, easily and gracefully. It occurred to me that those ten little somas were, quite likely, "without blemish." Certainly they were "peaceable" and "gentle." It seemed to me that they were "purely and genuinely themselves as they were destined to be."

Wasn't that what passed before my eyes? Fairness? And wasn't it possible that those precious creatures were already in the Fair

Realm? And I, the presumed philosopher, was outside of that realm, struggling to understand it, hoping that I could enter it?

I sorely needed to know what fairness was and what the Fair Realm was. Fred wanted me to know. That was what he was waiting for me to ask, "What is the Fair Realm?" I sensed that it might be the last question I would ask him, because it seemed the ultimate question—the one he had been leading me toward from the very beginning.

During these weeks, I had felt like a sack which Fred was gradually turning inside out. I first addressed him as someone who was "there," outside of me—but he spun me through the revolving door and instructed me to address him as a first-person entity who was "here."

The puzzle of it was that the only first-person entity I would ever know was myself. Fred was consistent in telling me that the only way I could come to know him was to know myself. It was tantamount to saying that I was Fred and that, somehow, Fred was I, which was not true.

What was true, however, was that I, an aware human being, had emerged in the most natural and inevitable way from the whole process of cosmic and biological evolution—which was another way of saying I had emerged from Fred. Like a "blossom," he said. I could fully understand that. But how much of me is Fred, and how much of me is me? Getting to know Fred meant getting to know myself. All right, but as I got nearer to knowing myself, did that mean nearer to being Fred?

Well, then, that was a troublesome thought: the exhilarating possibility of godly grandeur was one thing, but it was neatly counterbalanced by the clear possibility that I was being a deluded jackass. Or was that my ogre speaking again, telling me it is blasphemous to think of oneself as a god? The perspiration was not stinging my eyes, and I was not feeling feverish, but the perplexity I felt was almost as intense as it had been at the beginning.

But, I reminded myself, I was in the throes of digestion. I was in the process of absorbing into my being the immensity of what Fred had told me. That is what digestion is: the assimilation of a foreign ingredient into one's system. The foreign substance has to be broken down to fit one's system. Unfortunately, what Fred was telling me had to do with my system itself—that it was capable of far, far more than I had ever dreamed. So how was I to absorb into my system something which, in the process, was changing the system that was absorbing it?

A fine conundrum! But, all things considered, I did not mind it in the least. I was simultaneously confused and happy—and do you know what? I was thinking I would not mind staying that way.

How Do You Do?

Friday morning was chilly. The fog had managed to slip over the mountain, spreading a blanket of mist between the radiant warmth of the sun and the deep coolness of my valley. I turned on the heat in the study; then I went over to the bookshelf and slipped out the yellow pad. I noticed that its pages were beginning to fill up.

I had changed my mind about asking Fred the question, "What is the Fair Realm?" That seemed a bit academic. I decided it would be better to make the question both personal and practical. So, taking hold of the pen, I wrote:

Dear Fred:
  How do I get into the Fair Realm?
                              Yours,
                              Tom

I waited, listening to the sound of the heater. The feeling of movement slowly stole into my right shoulder and forearm. Then Fred's words came out like a quick, soft whisper.

Dear Tom:
  You are already in it.
                              Yours,
                              Fred

I sat, looking at the words, mildly stunned. The revolving door. The abrupt answer. Once again, Fred had pulled the rug out from under me.

I must have remained in a dazed state for a good two minutes, until the soft feeling of movement crept back again into my shoulder. Once more, the pen began moving:

Dear Tom:

Sorry about that. I couldn't resist it. After all, it was You who made the impertinent suggestion that I was a wag. If you ask a nonacademic question, You should expect a nonacademic answer.

But You get the point. Don't get Yourself worked up over how to get in. You are already in. That is the least of Your problems. The real question is what do You do now that You know You are in? Or, more precisely, not what, but how *do You do?*

You have always lived in the Fair Realm. You just have not always known it. That is why You needed to be reminded of Your past. For example, when You kissed the sidewalk, You were square in the middle of the Fair Realm. You knew how to be there. When You and Bubba soared into the teeth of the storm, You were in it then. In fact, during Your childhood there was rarely a time when You were not in the Fair Realm; but as You grew older, You did not always behave as if You were there. You had forgotten how.

Your adult learning was like the fog that came into Your valley this morning: it came between You and the light of Your past. But fog can burn itself off. That is what was happening when the work with Your clients became more transparent. The same thing was happening when You noticed Your walk becoming more fluid and effortless and the earth feeling different under Your feet. When everything in Your life becomes easier and more efficient, You are experiencing things moving fairly. You are learning how to smooth out the process of Your experience.

That is what was happening when You realized that You were becoming either more in connection with the world or, as You qualified it, in connection with more of the world. Certainly, that was what was happening when You got under the chair on Your mother's porch that second time. That was crazy. Of course, it was – but learning to navigate in the Fair Realm is like that: it is eccentric. It is supposed to be unpredictable. So, I have been helping You burn off the fog, freeing You to become more eccentric from the point of view of others "there," but more centric from Your own point of view "here."

When the mist is dissipated and the sky becomes fair again, everyone will be able to see how fair everything has always been. Everyone will be able to see that he has always floated along in a stream of things moving fairly – even though he himself has not always moved as fairly as the stream does.

The stream always moves fairly, but You, Tom, have spent a great deal of time in the middle of the stream thrashing about against the current and feeling that existential ache in Your gut. To be in the Fair Realm is to float in a stream that is very long. If You look behind You, there is nothing but water stretching back for uncountable miles. It is flowing forward from a source that is too far away to be visible but whose push and presence are so strong that You feel it intimately and constantly. The source never ceases to drive You forward.

The stream is – if You will excuse the expression – me. It is "things moving freely." The source is the Great Shout, which is where the stream began. Since You are somewhat in tune now, that should not be too hard to understand.

You were out on Your chaise longue again, nattering to Yourself that I had turned You inside out, like a sack, making You gaze inward rather than outward, urging You to look "here" rather than "there." That's right. As soon as You turned inward, what did You encounter? Your past. You found Yourself going "backward" and "downward."

Can't You see the inevitability of my curriculum? After all, what are You other than Your past? What are You other than Your experience? Remember what I said about awareness being like a mouth? What does it consume? Experience – swallow after swallow of experience, every swallow of which is remembered.

Your awareness, at this very moment, is Your remembered experience moving forward, accumulating more experience. Awareness always moves forward, just as the stream moves forward. The stream always moves forward fairly – You figured that one out after the bee dance: the whole space-time continuum is nothing but things moving freely. The question is whether Your awareness does the same.

You see, Tom, fairness is the undercurrent of all Your experience: You are immersed in the stream of my unfolding. The human task is to learn to unfold fairly.

In that regard, I am Your guide – Your model, if You prefer. I have no choice but to flow outward fairly, expanding as I do so into a limitless openness. There are no external limits to my expansion. My energy creates more and more matter – more "things"– which blossom outward, ever wider into the void.

I simply cannot help moving fairly. The particles of my being cannot avoid being totally efficient. They waste neither time nor effort in their mutual unfoldings. When You see the waters of an ocean move against a rock, You see fair movement. Everything follows the path of least resistance. Everything, in a sense, is honest and straightforward.

When things move fairly, they neither seek nor avoid conflict: they yield to the flow of inevitability. If things impact, they impact efficiently and unreservedly, so that the impact creates its own full aftermath – new light, new energy, a new direction of momentum. That is perfect adaptation.

When things move fairly, they do not pass other things without notice. No, they show their recognition of the other's presence by veering courteously in a discrete curve. The shape of the entire cosmos, with its sworls and orbits, is a graceful dance of courteous recognition of the other's presence.

Remember what I told You about the importance of families — that families are the foundation of human freedom and that individual freedom is a social product? Look at it on a cosmic scale. Think of the pattern of galaxies and constellations. Everything in space moves freely while maintaining certain patterns. Cosmology makes clear how things can move both freely and together.

Everything is inseparable because everything is part of the same stream of movement that began in that long-ago moment of the Great Shout. It was one at the beginning, and it is one now. All things are one, yet the one is composed of the many moving things — each having its own momentum and destiny; each owing its momentum to the past surging behind it; each guiding its destiny by adapting its momentum to the rules of social courtesy.

The Fair Realm is all around You. It surrounds and supports You. Its energy drives You forward. You have evolved from that surging stream as an awareness, unique in being able to control Your own destiny.

You, Thomas, are the unpredictable. You are the freedom of the universe — its adventure. Its eccentricity. There is nothing more interesting than You, the human, because with You anything is possible. Awareness not only creates reality, it is free to experience whatever reality it chooses. That is why anything is possible.

Let's pause for just a moment. I sense that You understand me, so I won't belabor the point. Let's stop and consider what was bothering You while You were thinking confusing thoughts on the chaise: what is the difference between me and You? What's the first thing that comes to mind?

Voilà! You've got it! Awareness. You are aware, and I am

not. Awareness is the burning center of Your process, eating its
way into the universe. You can experience, and I cannot. But,
then, where do I come in? What part of You was not created by
Your awareness?

I will give You five seconds: One, two, three . . . Good! Go to
the head of the class. You are smarter than You look. What
part of You is me? Your soma? Yes. Rather obvious, isn't it? You
did not create this sensory-motor process. You arose from it,
like the glow from a burning forge. Your "body" and the process which keeps it present "there" in the world is my doing.
Your awareness and the reality it experiences in the world is
Your doing.

I gave You Your soma and its original momentum. You came
into the world already primed for action, already needy, already
demanding what You wanted to sense and do. That is what I
mean by "momentum." The push of the past was already in the
heart of Your awareness. There was nothing passive about it,
even at the beginning.

With Your parents' help — and society's — You put together
Your initial awareness. You cultivated Your expectations of how
the world was, how others were, and how You could live in this
world with others.

That was Your first achieved experience — Your "first persona." That first persona was a shell — a shell You had to peck
and crack in order to hatch Yourself.

Every human has to free himself from that first, makeshift
shell. In the same way that my original momentum had to be
transcended by the Second Great Shout, so did the original persona of Your first learning have to be transcended. The momentum of Your first acculturation had to be corrected.

You should ask Yourself, "Why must this first momentum
and learning be corrected? Why do You feel such an urge to
free Yourself from it?" It is simply because You and all others
are already immersed in the Fair Realm. It carries You along,

It nurtures You with energy. It gives You bodily substance. It moves You forward relentlessly.

Moreover, it moves You forward freely, adapting and adjusting in the fair way that all streams move. That fair movement surrounds You. You are immersed in it. Its freedom penetrates every cell of Your being, freely adapting, rebalancing, self-healing – as long as You do not foul it up.

How can You avoid feeling the urge of freedom, since everything surrounding Your awareness is free process? To be human is to be haunted by freedom – born and baptized in it.

Here's the crucial point: You do not have to live freely. *That is the crux of the matter. To be free means that You can choose to become enslaved. To be free means that You can choose to live foully. You can deny the possibility of fairness in Yourself and in others. Freedom is the ability to deny freedom for Yourself and others.*

Makes sense, doesn't it? If You were not free to become enslaved, then You would not be genuinely free. But You are genuinely free. You can mock me and the cosmos. You can mock the fairness of all things moving freely in time and space. You are *free to embroil Yourself in a past that never changes, in habits that never crumble, in beliefs that never evolve, and in expectations that never expand.*

You can thrash about, fighting against the stream, exhausting Yourself, and deforming Your experience. That means a deformation of Your body, Your emotions, and Your thinking – the entire somatic process.

You can drag the cultural past along with You, repeating it ad infinitum. *That is Your freedom. Never forget that all You will ever be is Your experienced past and the attitude You take toward it. Your experienced past comes in three stages: the past I give You, the past Your culture gives You, and, finally, the past You give Yourself. If You live fairly, You will never cease transcending all three.*

You were wondering about the quail. Are they in the Fair Realm? Of course they are — in their own perfectly quail-like way. They are perfect, because they perfectly fulfill their fixed roles as quail. That is their nature. They automatically mesh their lives with all else, just as all other animals do. That's the social courtesy of the ecological realm. Animals cannot help living fairly. They are not free to be anything other than fair.

What about You, querulous king of the chaise longue, *with Your throbbing existential ache? What is Your nature? Clearly, it is very different from the quail's. Your role is not fixed. Your nature is to be free — to adapt fully the momentum of Your past with the potentialities of the present.*

Notice the paradox of freedom: You are nothing but Your past, yet adaptation demands that You be free to deny it at the drop of a hat. That is how electrons live. That is how flowing streams live. That is how galaxies live. That is how I live. How do You live?

You are the only being in the universe that is free to be as fair as the universe. The universe is nothing but things moving freely — that is the stream. Thus, You are the being who is free to be free.

O.K. You wanted to be "personal and practical." I don't mind accommodating You. Being in the Fair Realm is a way of living. *It is not a* what, *nor is it a* place. *It is a* how. *How do You take the momentum of Your own inheritance and Your own cultural parentage and develop it fairly so that it is "unblemished," "unbiased," "open," and "successful"? How can You achieve this while, simultaneously, being "gentle," "peaceable," and "easy"?*

Well, human freedom leaves You only one course: You must intend to be fair. *You* must expect it. *You* must hope it. *You must demand it. You must absolutely insist upon it. That is what Your freedom means.*

Nothing in Your past will ever justify You in freely intending the future. That is the nature of the past; it closes in upon itself and consolidates itself as a world of its own.

The "future"– what is it? It is blank. It is void. It is empty. It is yet to be fulfilled. Does that sound familiar to You? Who else expands outward into a blank, empty void, while attempting to fill it? Yes, me, Your old friend Fred, who has created Your soma, Your sensory-motor awareness, so that You could experience a reality of Your own creation.

Nothing will ever justify living in fairness. Freedom is its own justification. Freedom is the intention to fill the void of futurity. It eats its way into the void, creating something out of nothing. It is an eternal appetite with an eternal joy and satisfaction that is self-justifying.

Something else: freedom is not a burden. Only the past is. Freedom is just the opposite. It is a way of existing that frees You from the past. It has always been the only avenue of transcendence for humans. More than that, it is the very heart of religiousness. It is the faith that surpasseth the understanding of the human past.

What do You get for Your freedom? What does Your eccentric and audacious free intention create for You? Just one thing: experience – the exquisite taste of experience, the savor of reality that You have created. Isn't that all anyone ever wants – experience? Isn't that what drives everyone on, motivating them, inspiring them? Not to have something. Not to do something. But, rather, it is something infinitely more significant for all beings: to experience something – experience it, even if only for one moment. Entire lives have been justified and redeemed by a single experience – one awed glance, one delicate touch, one triumphant moment, one tender caress.

For most humans, just that is enough; and for some, even that is beyond their reach. For most humans, the burden of the past, of their ancestors, of their religions, of their customs, of *their treasured guilt lies upon them so heavily that the ineffably light movement of freedom is forever beyond their capacity. It is not freedom that is too heavy; on the contrary, it is the burdensome residue of a past that has nothing to do with present awareness.*

You are nothing but Your past experience. That is obvious. But You are also in time: namely, movement — or, more precisely, Your awareness is moving forward, driven by the momentum of the past. The future is void and empty, always waiting for Your intention. Your awareness is always "here," in the present, busily taking the residue of the past and thatching it with Your intentions for the future. The result of this process is the experience of reality.

Can't You see, Tom, that reality is not given, but taken? That is how it is for humans. Sticks and stones are fixed, natural laws are unchangeable, but experienced reality is what You make of it. If You believe You are fixed and unchangeable, then Your reality will be that way. You will get what You expect. In the end, all humans get what they expect. They are never disappointed.

If You expect disappointment, betrayal, failure, and sickness, You will get what You expect. If You expect fulfillment, love, success, and health, You will get it. Your expectation remolds Your past, creating the newness of the present moment.

Do You dare to expect the impossible? Do You dare to defy the tyranny of Your past? Do You dare to believe in Your infinite possibilities and capacities? Nothing in the past will justify that belief. No one around You will confirm Your infinite possibilities and capacities. No one, including me, can be in the center of Your Hereness and freedom.

In freedom, You are prodigiously solitary. You are serenely uncompelled. You are unattached from the past — and from me. You are purely Yourself — purely a centrum of action.

In freedom, You actualize what You have always falsely attributed to me: the divine power to create ex nihilo. In freedom, You become the God You have always – and rightly – believed to exist: the God who, all alone, creates the world.

Finally, that is what I meant when I said that You do not know who You are. That is the secret of Your power – the $E = MC^2$ of Hereness. What is it? Let's call it this: $F = AF^2$. It is *the formula for living in the Fair Realm: Fairness = Adaptability squared by Freedom.*

This is, as well, the formula for being totally "here" and not entrapped in Thereness. Thereness is fixed, like sticks and stones and natural laws. It is repetitive. The past is like that. Culture is like that. History is like that. Religious doctrines are like that. Even galaxies are like that. Nothing that is "there" ever justifies being fully "here." Nothing outside of Your present experience ever justifies Your present experience. It takes You away from it.

You are aware that You are living in a century which has given itself over to a religion of Thereness – with reality being reduced to objectivity and what is perceived as outside of You. You are living in an age of science that has replaced the God of Thereness with the factuality of Thereness. Religions of Thereness always deny Hereness.

Traditional religion defiles Hereness and awareness by claiming that they are corrupt and sinful. The new religion, science, defiles Hereness and awareness by claiming that they do not exist, for they are not factually provable. But, in both instances, they make the colossal error of ignoring that nothing whatsoever is "there" unless there is someone "here" who is aware of it. *Thereness depends totally on Hereness – otherwise, there is no theology, no matter how confused; nor is there any science, no matter how short-sighted.*

You have been crucified by Thereness, generation after generation. Think of it: millions and millions of little boys and girls

*spewing forth constantly from the bowels of the cosmos, all free
and fair, all unblemished and beautiful, savoring the experience
of their free and spontaneous intentions – and what happens?
They are plowed under. The fog comes over the mountains, and
their sense of me and my Fair Realm is obscured. Their vision is
clouded, and their reach is truncated. Their expectations are
restricted, and their self-image is defined, circumscribed, and
weighed down with limitation.*

*They become "adults," which is to say that they lose their
sense of me and of fairness. Thus, they lose their sense of who
they are and of what they are capable. They lose their future
and their transcendence. They are gradually stripped of their
courage and honor. They become cautious and fixed, knowledgeable and certain, boring and repetitious, foul and
unhealthy. They become polluted.*

*Sometimes, I become infinitely sad when I see what happens
to You. It makes me sad when children – who are my friends
and are so near to me – turn slowly away, their eyes glazed by
the hypnotic certainty which their parents and other adults have
about the "real world." Rather than doing what they do best –
being joyous and growing freely – they turn away from me, to
endure a slow, stultifying death, never suspecting they are being
polluted by what has been done to them in the name of reality,
God, goodness, truth, and science.*

*Each generation slowly murders the next. Generation after
generation, I must watch them turning away from me, growing
stagnant and moribund. Oh, Thomas, it is so dreadfully
unnecessary. I have never needed a son to demonstrate crucifixion; You have crucified Your own children since the beginning
of human history. You know not what You do. That is why You
have learned nothing from this perennial tragedy.*

*After all these millennia, I should think that some of You
would be sick of it. I should think that some of You would realize what You are doing to Yourselves and dare anything, risk*

everything to put an end to it – to make a hiatus between the unlimited capacity for human learning and self-transformation and the wretched business of allowing a humanly destructive culture to be imposed on innocent children who possess these unlimited capacities.

Don't You want grace for Your children? Don't You want them unblemished and wholly healthy? Don't You want them to grow and expand in fairness, cresting to fair horizons only to discover more horizons? Don't You want their awareness and their worlds to be unfixed and unlimited? Don't You want them to be with me, accepting me and my fair ways?

Why must You turn away from me? Can't You see that nothing in the entire sprawl of the cosmos is more important to me than You? Can't You see that there is nothing I want more than for Your awareness and Your freedom to grow to the maximum? Can't You see that there is nothing I care about more than You? Can't . . . can't You see . . . how much I need You . . . Oh! it breaks my heart how much I love You . . . .

My hand was trembling as it scrawled the last line. The letter stopped, but the trembling spread into the rest of my body like a possession. I began to shake. Then the feeling welled up and poured forth, and I gently put my face down on the yellow pad, sobbing with a sadness that seemed infinite.

The Pill Counter

I was in the drugstore, getting a few odds and ends, when something caught my eye. As I passed by the main counter, where the pharmacists worked, I noticed in front of it an entire section devoted to painkillers.

I stopped and looked at what was there. The collection of analgesic drugs was immense: myriad brand names, different chemical combinations, some "regular" and others "extra strength."

The display took up an amazing amount of space. I decided to measure it. I started at one end, placing one foot carefully in front of the other. One of the pharmacists eyed me curiously. I paced off twelve feet of counter space. Impressive. Then I noticed that the display turned the corner and continued for three more feet. I measured the height of the display against my own height. It was at least five feet tall. Five feet by fifteen feet: seventy-five square feet of painkillers!

That was food for thought. The pharmacist glanced at me again, but I ignored him. I was concerned about something else: the analgesic drugs were displayed in the most prominent place in the drugstore — stage center, by the pharmacist's counter.

I began to understand that I was standing in front of a significant cultural artifact. It was a seventy-five-square-foot monument to the suffering of my fellow citizens.

Even more was involved. These analgesics were *non-prescription* drugs. Behind that counter were all the *other* painkillers one could get with a doctor's prescription. The monument suddenly loomed bigger.

This display of drugs was in just one of several drugstores in a small town! Multiplied by all the other drugstores throughout the United States, the number is a mute—but stunning—public admission that the land of plenty and opportunity is a land where much of the population is in pain.

The pharmacist finally asked, "Can I help you?"

I said, "Do you know that you have seventy-five square feet of painkillers?"

"Humph," he said, continuing to put labels on bottles. "Didn't know that. Guess people must need 'em."

I guess they do. I left the drugstore, thinking how accurate Fred had been in describing the effect of our culture upon human lives.

I was still—three days later—weighed down by the poignant contents of Fred's letter. I do not think I would have noticed the monument to pain if he had not made the remark about people becoming "foul and unhealthy" as they unwittingly absorbed our cultural traditions. The most signficant things in life are the most obvious—such as seventy-five square feet of painkillers. It is the very obviousness and familiarity of these things that causes them to escape our notice. Fred was not only making me remember significant things from the past, but I was also beginning to notice significant things in the present.

When Fred spoke about the "soma," he meant the process of experiencing—our first-person awareness of ourselves. He had meant the experience of the body as well as everything else in our awareness. I could see that this was true: when we experience ourselves, we really cannot distinguish between what is mental or emotional or bodily. We are experiencing feeling. Some of those feelings are psychological, and some are physiological, but they are all part of the same process. If you foul up the process, you have fouled up the bodily and emotional process just as much as the mental.

The seventy-five square feet of painkillers seemed to be a massive confirmation of what Fred had said about the debilitating effects of our culture. His plaintive words resounded again in my consciousness: "Sometimes, I become infinitely sad when I see what happens to You." And he talked about how people "endure a slow, stultifying death, never suspecting what has been done to them in the name of reality. . . . " The pill counter was a crucifixion index that applied to the whole population.

All of this fitted in with what I had learned from working with the pained and stiffened bodies of my clients. From my knowledge of neurophysiology, I am aware that a person suffering chronic pain in the back and neck is not experiencing pain from something that has already happened in the past, but, rather, he is experiencing pain from what is continuing to happen right now in the present. The muscles in the back of such an unhappy soma are in constant contraction. It is an ongoing process, but the person is not aware of it. He cannot sense it, nor can he control it. He can only feel the result of it: pain. Muscles in constant contraction are constantly manufacturing lactic acid, whose presence in the muscle fibers irritates and burns the pain receptors, causing the experience of pain.

Physicians, because they see things only from the point of view of Thereness, make the mistake of diagnosing the problem as a structural breakdown. They see X-rays of a lower spine, with the vertebrae curved by constant muscular contraction, compressing the disks, and they falsely assume that the compressed vertebral disks are degenerating. What they do not see—because X-rays do not show muscles—is that the muscles are full of lactic acid from continual contraction and that the actual cause of the pain is the lactic acid in the muscles, not the disks.

I know this to be the case: simply by teaching my clients to become aware of their muscle contractions, they have learned to control the muscles and to relax them. Thereupon, the chronic pain has ceased because lactic acid is no longer manufactured.

As I crossed the parking lot, heading toward my car, I realized that by teaching clients to do this, I am giving them sensory awareness which leads directly to an increase in their motor control — namely, the ability to relax their muscles. But that was exactly what Fred was talking about! Awareness, he kept saying, was nothing but sensing and acting. The process of awareness is as much bodily as mental; if you make that process fairer and more efficient, you make the body comfortable again.

I opened the door of the car, got in, and sat there, looking out the window. There were two crows perched on the roof of the drugstore. I wondered if they were my crows.

I realized that what had seemed so portentous in Fred's last letter was indeed just that. What he said made sense of things I had been doing intuitively without understanding them. I could see that the reason I was successful in my work was that I was teaching people to become aware of their process. I was teaching them *how to do*. When their process ran fairly, they became comfortable again; not only that, but their bodies literally changed, and their postures were different.

Watching the people in the shopping mall, many of whom were entering the drugstore and perhaps heading for the counter of painkillers, it was clear how pain had entered their lives. Those pains in their backs were *cultural* in origin.

I know there is a reflex called the *Landau reaction* that automatically causes the posterior muscles to contract, erecting the back and readying the body for action. I know, also, that every time a telephone rings or one's name is called or there is a knock on the door, the Landau reaction is automatically triggered: muscles contract in the back, buttock, and hamstrings.

These are the typical areas of pain and stiffness in the businessman. By the time most men are in their forties, they have intermittent pain in these areas — the medical estimate is that it is as much as eighty per cent of the population. That's a crucifixion index. The typical business person in our society must respond promptly to many demands on his time (ringing telephones, visitors, emergencies, and so forth), year in and year out. It is not surprising that such continuous stressful activity creates a habitual contraction of the posterior muscles.

Now I can understand it. The acquired needs and learned ambitions of the culture create the bodily habits of the population. Those businessmen –"never suspecting"– had trained themselves to deal with the "real world." In this regrettable instance, the "real world" had befouled their somatic process.

It is not just the pain. It is worse than that: the overall day-to-day experience is befouled. That is why all those painkillers are available without prescription: they are considered the ordinary, day-to-day needs of the population to assuage the unhappiness of their conscious experience.

A woman passed in front of my car. She was stooped over as she walked; her shoulders were slightly rounded and raised, her chest was flat, and her neck was curved, with her face projected forward. I could see the protuberance of a "dowager's hump" in the back of her neck. She was only about fifty years old, but she looked elderly. More than that, her posture made her look depressed, defeated.

I knew that in her heart she vaguely felt depressed and defeated. It was a posture that was very familiar to me, for I had seen it thousands of times. It was the result of the habituation of another most common reflex: the startle reflex.

Looking at her, I again remembered Fred's words about joyous, spontaneous children gradually turning away from him as they adjusted to what they are told is the "real world." The sad, cringing figure passing by me was once a joyous little girl, full of enthusiasm; but as she became an adult, she learned to worry and be anxious about the important realities of the adult world. Lord knows, a few evenings of the ten o'clock news, and you have enough tragedy and misery to last a lifetime. The anxiety of worry is a direct cause of the startle reflex. Over the years, her constant fretting had gradually established her habitually stooped posture.

I did not start the car, but remained there in the parking lot, watching my fellow adults pass by as they headed for the drugstore. The crows also watched. As I looked closely at the passersby, I noticed that almost all of them had clear traces of either the Landau reflex or the startle reflex. I also noticed that most of them had a combination of both reflexes: a little sway-backed, yet a little stooped in the upper body—the typical, middle-aged adult.

Like the pill counter, the appearance of these adults was so obvious and familiar that it was, in a sense, invisible. It was the culture itself that I saw exemplified in their bodies, for our culture is the transparent environment in which our lives are immersed.

Fred was talking about bodies as well as minds and hearts. The traditional religions do not do that. They talk about souls. They want to save souls, but they do not care about bodies. It is O.K. for bodies to be crucified—so long as the soul is saved.

The scene in the parking lot and the vision of the pill counter came together as a single drama. Hovering above this drama was the sound of Fred's voice, saying, "After all these millennia, I should think that some of You would be sick of it. I should think that some of You would realize what You are doing to Yourselves and dare anything, risk everything to put an end to it—to make a hiatus between the unlimited capacity for human learning and self-transformation and the wretched business of allowing a humanly destructive culture to be imposed on innocent children who possess these unlimited capacities."

After awhile, the crows took flight and disappeared. I started the engine and drove away.

To Hell
with Fred

At noon on Tuesday, I came home from the office, put on my shorts and Adidas, and went out on the patio to skip rope. I started slowly, jumping simultaneously with both feet. Then, as I warmed up, I slipped over into a pattern alternating between two legs: two hops on the left, two hops on the right, two hops on the left, and so on.

After five minutes, I changed over into a running pattern—an easy lope with the skipping rope cutting under the rise of my advancing left foot, just as the right foot is pushing off in back; as it begins lifting, the rope continues its arc, slipping beneath the right toes and rising upward again.

Later, I let the right foot lead. Rope skipping is an excellent way of observing oneself from within—proprioceptively. The repetitive, cyclical movements are perceived stroboscopically: by focusing attention on a knee or elbow or ankle and by observing its constantly repeated movements, you can gain a clearer appreciation of what is happening in that part of your body.

The experience of repetitive movement is in itself enlightening. Gradually, the action of running becomes mechanically transparent: the left leg reaches out and then moves under me and backward, making a half circle; just as the left foot lifts off the ground, the right foot descends to complete the cycle with its own half circle.

Running, from a first-person perspective, is the experience of circularity. It gives us the awareness of rolling along the ground with a left half-wheel and a right half-wheel. Because the repeated movements offer a continuous sensory picture of what each body part is doing, we can keep a precise check on the relative ease and balance of our movements.

I think Fred would approve. It is a way of monitoring the efficiency of one's bodily movements and of moving more fairly. How does my foot strike the ground? In comparison, how does the opposite foot strike the ground? Does one foot strike harder than the other? More on the outside or on the inside of the sole? Is the toe of one foot turned more inward? By this method of observation, I can learn to equalize my gait. I teach myself to become self-correcting.

Does the right elbow move forward and backward much more than the left elbow? Or the reverse? Compare how the left shoulder, rib cage, and pelvis move in contrast to the right side. Do you notice that the left arm is not only moving less than the right but that the left leg is also moving less? If that is the case, it is likely that all of the left side is involuntarily holding itself in contraction more than the right.

Rope skipping had become, for me, an exercise in self-awareness and self-discovery — simple discoveries which become essential insights in learning to live more efficiently. Life becomes easier, less onerous, and — I now realized — fairer.

After ten minutes of skipping, I felt perspiration gathering on my brow. Sunlight glanced off the skipping rope, its blurred contours encircling me like a glistening cocoon. My breath held into an easy, slower counterrhythm to my gait. I imagined I was a steam locomotive — the air puffing in and out, the pistons of the long bones driving back and forth, and the joints circling like cogwheels.

I stopped, breathing heavily, my eyes gazing upward at the acacia trees on the hill. A little whippet of breeze went by, briefly cooling me. I waited for another. It came and tossed my hair about, the coolness fingering my scalp.

There was a strange odor in the breeze. I sniffed. I sniffed again, but the odor was not there this time. I turned my head left and right. Another small breeze came, and the unpleasant odor came again. I knew what it was: the smell of an animal carcass rotting—most likely, a dead gopher that the neighborhood dogs had left in my yard.

I walked over to the junipers and sniffed around, but there was no odor. I went behind the junipers and searched there, but still found nothing. I opened the gate into the side yard, and then I smelled the odor again—this time it was stronger. In front of me was a large blackberry patch, which occupied the middle portion of the side yard.

I walked slowly along the sides of the patch, looking into the heavily thorned vines. As I was bent forward, scrutinizing the tangle of vines, a crow suddenly flew over my head. It came so close to me that, when it let out its sudden rasping caw, I jumped. A tingle of fear shot through me.

The odor was strong, but still I could not find its source. As I walked around to the other side of the blackberry bushes, the stench became overwhelming. Looking down into the thicket, I saw a body lying on the ground. It was a young doe, eyes still open, as if watching me serenely. There were flies on her face and eyelids. Clearly, she had been dead for several days, for the decomposition was advanced.

Then I saw something else. Next to the doe, touching her, was a just-born fawn—also dead. My eyes were riveted to the scene. The delicacy and gentleness of the doe's staring countenance was devastating, and the fawn lay there, a ghostly half-presence of pink and gray protoplasm still bearing its fetal envelope.

I was afflicted by the uncanny and tragic beauty of what I was seeing. The young doe was, surely, a sister to the young buck I had seen a week or so ago. She had come to this place to have her fawn and die. It must have seemed a safe resting place. She lay there so quietly, graceful even in her stillness; her fur was only a bit darker than the parched turf on which she lay.

I could look no longer. The poignancy of the doe's eyes gazing so softly at me was unbearable. I moved away from the blackberries, walking downward toward the creek, then crossing over to the wooden fence which ran along the road. I felt a pang around my eyes, just above the cheek bones, as if I had been smitten.

I walked by the fence where a tangled vine of roses was still blooming. As I came to the gate, my gaze was focused upward at the roses. That is why I did not see what was in my way until I stepped on it. As soon as my foot felt what was under it, I jumped. It was a recoil of horror. My heart began pounding, and the area around my eyes began to harden.

I could not believe it. Beneath my eyes was the freckled body of one of the young fawns that had invaded my yard a few weeks previously. He was lying flush against the gate, curled inward upon himself. I had no idea what to think.

Then I began a systematic search over all the property to see if there were other dead deer. Two minutes later, I found another young buck under the plum trees. I continued looking, but found no others.

It took several phone calls before I located someone who could haul the carcasses away. Late that afternoon after I had returned from work, a man came by in a pickup truck and piled the four bodies into the back. He told me he had already hauled away forty deer that week. Some disease had stricken the deer population. He said that some people blamed it on the torrential rains during the previous winter.

He closed the back of the truck, got in the cab, and drove away. I watched as he drove slowly down the hill, finally to disappear around the curve. I became aware that the smitten feeling around my eyes was still there. It was not as if I were about to cry. It was a stunned feeling, as if someone had struck me. It was like a hurt that precipitates anger.

I walked back into the front yard and entered the house. I did not know what to do. I sat down in the living room, looking straight ahead at the wall. I remained that way for a long time, not feeling anything, not even thinking anything.

The afternoon light waned, and a coolness stole into the room. I was reminded of a late afternoon long ago when coolness flowed through into the windows of my brown cottage and splashed onto the floor. I could remember the undulating colors of the rug and the forlorn feelings of that hushed moment when I was sitting on the floor with Jean-Baptiste and Luke.

It was the same trancelike state, and I felt that same familiar ache, slowly throbbing in my core. It was an ancient wound—a painful wrongness that could not right itself and heal. It was the apprehension of a discord at the heart of all things—an unresolved tension that called everything into question.

And I felt like a small and useless creature: a tiny, helpless child, sitting in a chair too big for him. Nothing fit me. I was out of place in the chair, in the living room, in the house, in the world. My existence did not fit into any of it. I existed, yet I had no real place in existence—no fixed and lasting place.

I existed, just as those precious deer had existed, but they did not have a permanent place in existence—they were gone. What was the point of it? Why should they have been ushered into being when existence was not a permanent state?

They had lived in the Fair Realm, hadn't they? And what did it get them? Obliteration. They were graceful. They were efficient. They did not have blemishes. That's over now. They were dead. So, what is the good of a Fair Realm if everyone's going to die anyway?

Was it just so Fred could have what he was missing—awareness?

Was existence just a way for Fred to use me, the deer, and everyone else for his own purposes, as if we were all pawns to his grandiose schemes? Wasn't that what existence was—an endless parade of expendable beings, serving their turn and then disappearing as other hapless pawns took their place?

Fred talks about freedom and growth and expectation. He talks about the wonders of fairness, but not about death and disintegration and nothingness. There is nothing fair about dying. It is foul, and the Fair Realm is a fraud. At its heart, it rests on foulness.

The living room had become deadly cold and still. It reminded me of a morgue. The bleakness I felt was not in me. It was physically around me, palpable in the air itself, pressing inward against me—a stiffling pressure. I did not belong here. I did not feel I belonged anywhere. I, too, was expendable.

I got up and walked out of the living room into the kitchen. The yellow pad was lying on the table, where I had been rereading the last letter.

I sat down and picked up a pen. I ignored the established protocol and asked Fred a direct question:

Dear Fred:
  Why must I die?

                              Yours,
                              Tom

The reply came instantly:

Dear Tom:
  Because You were born.

                              Yours,
                              Fred

The flippancy of the reply infuriated me. It felt like a slap in the face. My eyes—already taut with hurt—sprang open with tears of rage. The cheeky audacity of such a reply was intolerable.

My jaw was hard and clenched, and I picked up the pen and began writing:

Dear Fred:

How dare you speak to me in such a manner. I came to you with a question that was more important than any of the other questions I have asked you. And you reply by being insulting.

It is all very well being an aware human being and experiencing things that you cannot experience. It is very flattering. I am not going to be aware very long, for I'm going to die, and my awareness is going to die with me. But there are other humans, aren't there? So, I'm expendable. Your great cosmic adventure will go on, using up other people. I am sure it will be a grand show, but I will not be around to enjoy it. Nor will anyone else for very long.

If I am going to die, then all of what you have told me is just tripe. It does not matter. It is not worth a damn. I will tell you one thing: using me for fodder is already abominable, but being flip about it is intolerable. I say: "To hell with you!"

Tom

I sat at the table as the light waned. The skylight that opened just over the dining area was a muted gray, and it left the kitchen gloomy and silent.

There would be no reply to this letter, nor would there be any more letters. In one stroke, I had broken the contact with Fred.

Crows were assembling over the house with their evening circles. The cacophony of their strident sounds made a sonorous lamentation. Today, four deer were gone. On another day, I too would be gone. Fred was already gone.

The silent kitchen was heavy with misery, and my heart

thumped a slow, sad beat. I was hurting, and I was angry. Fred was gone, but I did not miss him. I had rejected him. To hell with him! He could keep his fucking Fair Realm.

I picked up the yellow pad and threw it against the kitchen wall with all my strength.

Confrontation
under the Moon

I wanted no supper that evening. Instead, I opened a bottle of brandy and spent the evening drinking and raging inside. By eleven o'clock, the sad fury was slightly abated. It no longer tore at me. The bottle was three-quarters empty. I went to sleep in the living room chair.

In the middle of the night, I awoke. I felt a presence in the room. I listened intently, not moving. It must have been a sound that brought me awake, but now I heard nothing. There was only silence, but the feeling of a presence remained.

Could it be a prowler or burglar? Since I had gone to sleep without leaving any lights on, an intruder might have mistakenly thought no one was at home. But I wasn't afraid. I was strangely untroubled, as if the earlier sadness and anger had cauterized me of fear.

The more I listened, the more I was certain it wasn't a prowler. There was no one either in the house or outside.

Then I heard a small sound—just barely detectable. It came from the kitchen. Was it the refrigerator starting up? A drip from the faucet? No, it was something else—an indefinable sound, like a vague rustling.

I listened carefully. The silence stretched out, but the sound was not repeated.

I got up from the chair slowly, so as not to make a noise, and walked quietly into the kitchen. The entire room—dismal before —was now glowing in the moonlight that flooded down through the skylight, highlighting the dining-room table.

As I looked around, I became aware of an incongruity. The soft light poured over the surface of the table and down onto the floor, outlining everything in sharp contrast. Clearly, something was out of place, but I could not tell what it was. It took me a full minute to realize that the yellow pad was no longer on the floor where it had landed when I hurled it against the wall, but on the table with the pen neatly at its side, both glowing in the moonlight.

Bewildered, I pulled out the chair and sat down in front of the yellow pad, staring at its familiar form. It was powerfully luminous in the moonlight. This time, its blank surface was not ebbing and flowing in front of my gaze or slowly flapping around like the huge yellow butterfly I had once hallucinated. Its potent presence was once again pressing inward toward me.

The yellow pad—that was the presence I had felt in the house. But its presence was Fred's presence, which meant that he had not disappeared. Contact had not been lost.

At the instant I thought this, the muscles around my shoulder blade softly contracted. Fred was about to communicate. My hand went to the pen, lifted it, and began writing:

Dear Tom:

Now You have shown me both sides of the coin — the two sides You humans typically show me. At first, when You knew nothing about me, You tried to grovel and beg forgiveness. Remember? And, now that I have started to reveal myself to You, You say, "To hell with you!"

It is not only impolite; it is inconsistent. But it is typical of Your race and its culture. You vacillate between groveling and rebelling, but those two sides of the cultural coin show just how cockeyed and fouled up Your awareness has become. You have drunk too heavily of Your cultural intoxicant, and it has distorted Your perception.

So, doubting Thomas, what am I to do with Your rejection of me? Forgive You? Ah, You would like that, wouldn't You? Then You could grovel and start the cycle again. No, You don't merit forgiveness; that would be like throwing Br'er Rabbit back into the briar patch.

See how groveling and rebelling are linked together? Both are disjunctions in relationship – pitifully inefficient ways of relating. That is a poor use of Your freedom, isn't it? You are free to do such things, of course, but don't You think it is childish? Isn't such thrashing about becoming tiresome?

What would You say to the possibility of getting out of this boring rut and attempting to establish a more balanced relation with me – one of equality, for example? Does that seem too extreme?

Listen, I'm not proposing a radical revision – not a turnabout of one hundred and eighty degrees. How about a change of just ninety degrees? After all, that is, more or less, what I have been suggesting to You all along.

You see, a turnabout in our relation of ninety degrees is not a total revision, but only half a revision. As I become, as it were, fifty per cent "less" than before and as You accept Yourself as fifty per cent "more" than before, we can meet each other with equality. Then nobody has to grovel, and there is no need to rebel. A rather nice possibility, don't You think?

You do understand – don't You? – that when I speak of a change in relation to me, I mean to the world in general. What You have been stuck with culturally is an attitude that imputes too much to the world and, by consequence, too much to me.

All of Your so-called "advanced societies" are afraid of the world. You are paranoid. You think the world is Your enemy –

that it withholds its sustenance from You and that it is conspir-
ing against You. You believe that the world has to be attacked
and mastered – that it offers too little, leaving You in scarcity.

The unrealistically negative awareness You have of the natu-
ral world "there" outside of You goes hand-in-hand with the
unrealistically positive awareness You project of the supernatu-
ral "God" that is also "there" outside of You. For centuries, You
have been living with a negative world that is all too tangible
and with a positive god that is all too intangible.

You rebel against nature and You grovel before supernature.
More often than not, You get it all confused and grovel before
kings, priests, and posturing politicians who always take on the
supernatural aura of gods. At other times, You cynically rebel
against whatever You think is "God," either because You think
"God" impotent or unprovable.

What a crushing bore this all is! It is foul to the lowest
degree, and it gets You nowhere. A culture tells You what to
expect. It is the carrot-and-stick of awareness that tells You
how to go into the future. If You are taught to be paranoid
about the world, You cannot go forward into the future with the
smooth flow of Fairness; instead, things go jerkily – everyone
thrashes about.

Your traditional conception of "God" is the flip side of Your
conception of nature. In order to balance Your excessive para-
noia about nature, You project an untouchable, intangible being
who is all the things that nature is not. That is how it is, You
know: "God" is everything the world is not. That is why the
function of "God" in theology is to justify, rectify, and save
humans from the world.

But what if You revise Your presumptions about the world
and "God" ninety degrees? That improves Your estimate of the
world fifty per cent, and it lowers Your estimate of "God" fifty
per cent. By the same token, it raises Your own self-estimation

fifty per cent. At that moment parity reigns, and everything comes into focus. The world becomes what it has always been: the gift of opportunity. Humans become what they have always been: the beneficiaries of this gift.

What happens to the untouchable, intangible "God"? Nothing. It becomes what it has always been: nothing.

But, You ask, what happens to our sense of the ultimate? The ultimate becomes not a what *– a finalized being – but a* how *– an ongoing, ever-present process: the sensing and doing of Fairness.*

That is what You can expect to happen if You start expecting the best rather than the worst. You experience me as I really am: as both "here" and "there." I am as much You as I am the world. I am both – but I am both as a moving, ongoing process.

There You sit, Thomas, like Pierrot in the moonlight – "Prêtez-moi ta plume!"– scornful of me, and cynical about Fair Realms and death. It is true that You must die because You were born, just as it is true that I am "here" as well as "there." You have got Your focus on the wrong thing. The cosmos was not created just so that life could come into being. That is not the point. It was not only life, but awareness that was intended when the Great Shout occurred.

Birth and death are the polarities of life, but awareness involves something else. Awareness is a great loom that weaves the fabric of reality. Its warp and woof are sensing *and* doing: *sensing literally takes the world into the realm of the soma; doing literally takes the soma out into the world.*

Sensing and doing weave the world and the soma together into the reality that all humans experience. At some point, sensing and doing may cease their weaving – that is death – but it has absolutely nothing to do with what has been woven. Awareness continues. How could it not, since it consists of those parts of the world that have been woven into reality?

Death means that awareness continues in its achieved state and not in its achieving state. What is real remains real. What is individual remains individual.

I hope you do not think I would spend fifteen billion years evolving awareness into being if it were not the ultimate product of the entire cosmos. It is. You are — and You will continue to be.

Do not worry about how that can be. You do not even know how the quantum universe can be what it is. But it is. It does not take faith to accept a paradoxical fact — just honesty.

Besides that, do not think that the end of Your process is something tragic. It just is. That is another paradoxical fact that we share in common: my process will come to an end, just as Yours will. That is the effect of what science calls the entropy of the universe: movement burns up energy.

My energy will, some day, be exhausted. At that point, all movement will cease and all process will stop. We are both dying, Thomas. My death will simply take a bit longer than Yours. Then time and space will have their fulfillment: there will be nothing but awareness.

Awareness is eternal. It was implicit at the beginning. It will be explicit at the end. And the process of moving from beginning to end is a blessed and fair journey.

Can You accept this process? Can You accept me as I really am and Yourself as You really are? Can You accept our equality? Can You accept the responsibility that freedom offers? Do not be afraid of the responsibility: its reward is pride — the immense pride of being fully an individual.

Can You accept this inevitable movement of Fairness, stretching from beginning to end? The Great Shout was a shout of joy. Existence began in joy, continues in joy, and will terminate in joy.

I have said enough. You have drawn from me all that You need. You do not need to know any more. You only need to live more. But, can I ask You something? It is something personal I did not want to say until we had gotten to this point in our relationship.

If You have accepted me as Your equal and Yourself as my equal, that means we are friends; and if we are friends, then I can ask this very special favor. It is this: knowing now what You know about Yourself, about the world, and about me, can You forgive me for the way I am? Can You forgive me for all that I have done and could not help doing? Thomas, can You forgive What Is?

If You can do so, it will set my heart at ease. My heart is Your heart, Thomas. And if You can forgive me, You will lose, once and for all, the ache you have felt for so long. Then, Your heart will also be at ease.

> *Yours,*
> *Fred*

I put down the pen and stood up. I held myself erect and addressed him at eye level.

I said, "Yes, Fred, I forgive You. And I also forgive myself for who I am and all I have done."

Then I added, "It's *all* right!"

The Ducks
and the Geese
Know the Secret

Not only did I miss supper that night, I also missed sleep. The moonlight invading the kitchen had also entered my flesh. I did not want to part from its soft radiance. It was an ethereal liquid that seemed to be inviting me outside to bathe in it.

I looked at the kitchen clock. It was an hour before dawn. I put on a sweater and went outside to the car. The sky above was totally clear. Fred's far-flung body was so spread out above me that each of his cells glistened. I drove down the winding road, past the houses of my sleeping neighbors, and went to the main route leading westward out of town.

On all sides of me, the landscape glowed eerily. Under the patient moon, the black shadows beneath the oaks and bays were indistinguishable from the trees themselves. Surrounding the trees, dry grass—moon-bleached with whiteness—etched stark lines around the black forms, so that an abstract tableau swirled by me as I drove in the direction of the lake.

The road slowly rose up the valley, following the contours of a deep creek. Up ahead, I saw the dam. Eventually, the lake appeared, its surface mirroring the starry sky above. The view was so compelling that I parked the car, hopped over the fence, and walked across the grass toward the water.

Small oaks and willows guarded the lake. Picnic tables and fireplaces were scattered here and there. There were hundreds of ducks and geese gathered along the shore. Some were sleeping and others were moving about. The play of lights on the water was matched by the play of small quacks and honks in the air.

I walked a hundred yards before I came to the water's edge. I moved slowly, so as not to disturb my quacking neighbors assembled only twenty yards away. There was a picnic table under the shelter of a willow, and I sat down. An impressive scene lay before me. From the bowl of the lake, small mountains rose up, each rounded curve topped by the next, as the restless land ascended to the crest of a high mountain—a cluster of lumpish babies nestled around their mother.

The moon-white lines of the arching hilltops and the black lines of their shadows created a mosaic of half circles rising from water to sky. Down below, there were dancing sparks of light on the water; up above, there were serene dots of light in the sky; and, in-between, there was an intricate pattern of glowing curves. It was a nocturnal world of enchantment. I was happy I had accepted the moon's invitation.

The highest range of mountains was to the east, and over their crest was a gentle glow: my Earth was tilting into the dawn. Six migrating ducks, necks stretched long, dropped slowly from the sky and approached the lake like a flight of descending arrows. Just as they were about to touch down, their heads lifted up and their feet stretched downward, flattening against the air to break their speed just as they hit the water. Six little plunking sounds were followed by a series of satisfied quackings. They proceeded to paddle about, ducking their bills into the water.

The air on the lake was ineffably sweet. Its moisture filled my nostrils, and its chill lay on my skin. I looked down at my hands: they *were* bathed in moonlight. The cool light shimmered on my skin; simultaneously, the chill air caressed it. I became acutely aware of my enclosed presence: a solitary being in a self containing envelope, who was sitting in the midst of a vast moonlit landscape.

The feeling of my skin separating me from the outside world made me focus inward; as soon as I had done so, I became conscious of something unusual—something I had not felt for so long that I had almost forgotten it. It was a feeling from my childhood: a delicious feeling of wholeness—of all my pieces being in place.

I was experiencing myself as I had once been: innocent. The ancient ache which had separated me from that primitive wholeness for so long had vanished. I was once again myself, as birth and genes had intended me to be. There was no dissonance, no disfigurement or foulness—I felt only harmony, only fairness.

I realized that I had lived my entire adult life with a mute sense of grievance against the world—an unspoken grudge against existence. That was the dissonance—the disfigurement. During my adulthood, whatever I had done and experienced that was good had somehow been tainted with an accusation against reality that had prevented me from opening myself fully to the world.

The foulness that had infected my being was not something from my childhood. There was no Oedipal guilt and anger—only a feeling of love for my mother and father and an equally happy feeling for the forces of individuation that had wafted me away from their primal love.

The existential ache had not come from my biological past, but from my cultural past that had denied my wholeness and innocence. It had come from an adult world that had run roughshod over my first experience of myself and my reality.

I was all right. It was not I who was foul. It was the adult world that was not all right. I had given my innocent allegiance to that world, believing it to be whole and good. I had inherited a world that was fouled by its beliefs in original sin, in the evil of desire, in the distastefulness of exuberance, in the inappropriateness of honesty, in the wrongness of individual exploration, and in the danger of freedom. In short, it was a world of adult presumptions that denied everything of value I had experienced as a child.

The coolness of my skin reminded me of my separateness—my irreducible individuality. The wholeness and innocence I was feeling was the original experience I had had of my Hereness—of the raw thrill of being a Self, of the indescribable joy of having the chance to exist, to be aware, and to experience my Self and the world.

For the first time since childhood, I was experiencing myself as being fully "here." I am "here" at this table. I am "here" on this grass. I am "here" on this lake shore. I am "here" within this bowl of leaping mountains. I am "here" under this infinite canopy of burning suns and swirling constellations. I am "here" again with Fred, just as I had been during the sweetness of my childhood.

Hereness is not shallow; it is immeasurably deep and vast—far more so than Thereness. Thereness is only one-dimensional: it is the present—it is now. But Hereness encompasses all that has been, all that is, and the momentum toward all that may be. Hereness reaches beneath and behind the wall of Thereness, making what is "there" familiar—making it my own, taking possession of it. In my Hereness, I am as much behind the facade of Thereness as I am before it. My Hereness encompasses everything.

In the fullness of the "here" is the fullness of the cosmos, yet this is nothing other than the fullness of my Self. The cosmos *is* me, and I *am* the cosmos. In taking possession of myself, I had taken possession of the cosmos. It isn't *the* world; it is *my* world.

This world is my home. It has always been my home, since the beginning of time. I *belong* "here." I *belong* "there." And, in that belonging and interconnectedness, I experience the quantum nature of my awareness: awareness, in its fullness, is everywhere and every time.

I wasn't sitting at a picnic table in the moonlight. Like the ducks, I was floating. I was floating on my universe, freely and without effort, and I felt its fathomless support beneath me. I floated in utter balance with the center of the earth, feeling its core as clearly as I felt my skin. I could feel through the Earth to that balancing point where its great body held into the sun. I could feel how the Earth's solar system held in balance with its galaxy of the Milky Way. I could feel beyond that the balance of my galaxy with the entire metagalactic system as the material universe expanded outward from its original centrum. And I could feel my balance directly over that central core out of which the Great Shout had roared, expressing the cosmos and expressing its intention that I should, one day, be "here" and be aware of that primordial expressiveness.

In the moonlight, I floated over all space and all time, feeling their oneness, and knowing that the wholeness and innocence I felt were not only of myself, but also of my universe.

I really did not know if I were Fred or Fred were I, and I really did not care. I chuckled. Everything was all right. It had always been all right. It was all so simple. You did not have to figure it out. All You had to do was experience it. It was already "here," and it had been "here" since the moment of my birth.

I felt wonderful, floating on my picnic bench. I looked at the bobbing ducks and geese. I knew that they felt the same as I. They didn't need to be told about it. They experienced what I experienced. They were co-conspirators. They were not quacking: they were laughing.

I began to laugh out loud. That caused the rest of the ducks and geese to leave the shore and go into the water. Now everyone was floating and quacking and honking. I laughed and quacked with them. They knew the secret—they had always known what I had spent my entire adult life trying to recapture.

Dawn began pouring over the mountains to the east. It spilled into the lake, daubing it with pink. From the west, came flocks of gulls and bands of crows, wheeling down from the sky and landing on the shore. The gulls had come from the bay, and I was quite sure that the crows had come from the rookery up my hill. They joined in the cacophony. I laughed, the crows laughed, the gulls laughed, the ducks laughed, and the geese laughed. The hooting and cawing and quacking and honking filled the bowl of the valley and rose up into the mountains.

I had never been so happy. And I had never been so tired. I felt I was not so much floating as sinking. I badly needed sleep.

I trudged across the grass and back to the car, driving home half asleep. When I walked into the house, I went straight to the kitchen and stopped in front of the yellow pad, continuing to enjoy my happiness through the veil of fatigue. I put my hand on the yellow pages and, looking down, saw something that abruptly brought me awake. A pang coursed through my chest: there were only three blank sheets left. The correspondence was about to end. I was about to lose contact with Fred.

Efficient
to the End

J ean-Baptiste and Luke were my benefactors. They had left me
a magic yellow pad—a yellow pad which had brought me back
to my senses and restored me to myself.

The yellow pad was a priceless gift, and now it was all but used
up. I had been so taken by the magic that it never occurred to me
the bright summer of my enlightenment would come to a close.

I was about to say farewell to a friend. I did not wish to. The
thought of it cast a shadow over my freshly won happiness. During
these few weeks, so quickly flown by, I had come to depend on
Fred. With each letter, he had inched nearer to me, as I had inched
nearer to him and to myself. Now that we had come together, we
had to part.

I was no longer tired. I stood in the kitchen's morning light,
dumbstruck, staring at the three remaining sheets of yellow
paper. There was no sense in dragging it out. If I waited, it would
only make me unhappy, and I did not wish that. I had had enough
unhappiness for one lifetime.

So, I sat down and wrote:

Dear Fred:

*Thank you for your friendship, and thank you for letting me
come to know you. I do not wish to say goodby.*

*I know that I was a slow and difficult pupil, but I hope you have
seen that I can learn.*

With my whole heart, I can say that I am
                              Yours,
                              Tom

My pen never paused. It continued writing:

Dear Tom:

*How fitting that last night we were thinking about the end of
things! I do not wish to say goodby either.*

*After all, there is no way for us to say goodby because there
is no way for us to part. I am "here" to stay — as close to You as
the shirt on Your back. I just will not be communicating quite so
directly. Once the communication ends, it is most likely that You
will be left wondering if all this was really a communication with
me or only Your hallucination — just as You must be wondering if
I really did pick up this yellow pad last night. Or was it You and
the brandy? Am I right?*

*Communication with me certainly has its problems. I recog-
nize that. It is well-nigh impossible to distinguish between hallucination and reality when only one person experiences it. Yet,
that is the only way I can communicate: in Hereness — purely in
the first-person realm and never with more than one individual.
That makes it more interesting, don't You think? You know it is
not an illusion, but no one else can know this because they
cannot have Your first-person experience. Your experience is
"here," inside Your skin.*

*I cannot be "there" for all the world to see, since I am only
"here" for individual awareness to experience. My objective,
cosmic body, with its mundane features, is all that can be seen of
me in the third person, but my individual nature can never be
disclosed in that manner. That is the way it is, so do not let it be
a bother to You.*

Indeed, it is rather amusing, don't You think? That we have communicated is a fact. But, if You were so foolhardy as to tell others about it – insisting on this fact – just watch the odd, cautious look that will come into their eyes. They will suspect that Thomas is off his rocker. For heaven's sake, do not tell them that You kiss sidewalks, fly with magic porch chairs, or start Your mornings laughing with ducks and geese. If You do, they will know for sure that You have stripped Your gears.

You are alone with Your knowledge of me; but, on the other hand, because of this knowledge of me, You are never alone. Think about that: no matter what happens in Your life, from this point onward, You will never be lonely. I shall always be with You, just as I always have been –"here" on the edge of Your awareness.

So, it is not as if the yellow pad is finished and I am disappearing. We do not need to say adieu. It is only that I shall not be as verbal as I have been during these weeks of our relationship.

Now that we have finished our little chat, I'm going to slip back under the covers where I belong. You will cease to know me as "you, Fred," as I slip back into being "You, Thomas," lurking in the background. But, of course, I will still be "here," snugly nestled under the covers. Just poke the bedding, and You will feel my bones and sinew underneath. That will be me on the other side of Your touch. Once You know me, You will find me everywhere.

Remember now: You are the best thing about me – the best thing happening in my life. And I hope You will feel that I am the best thing happening in Your life. We belong together, You know, like brothers and friends – just like You and Bubba. You and I are a remarkable pair, once we have come to know each other.

O.K., now. Get ready: I am going to pull up the covers and pop under. Do not be afraid. Everything is all right. Remember:

I have not gone away. I am always "here," just as I am always
Yours,
Fred

Fred was very efficient as a letter writer. He ended on the last remaining line of the yellow pad.